The Energy Debate

ISSUES
(formerly Issues for the Nineties)

Volume 54

Editor

Craig Donnellan

Independence
Educational Publishers
Cambridge

First published by Independence
PO Box 295
Cambridge CB1 3XP
England

British Library Cataloguing in Publication Data
The Energy Debate – (Issues Series)
I. Donnellan, Craig II. Series
333.7'9

ISBN 1 86168 157 7

Printed in Great Britain
The Burlington Press
Cambridge

Typeset by
Claire Boyd

Cover
The illustration on the front cover is by
Pumpkin House.

CONTENTS

Chapter One: Energy Alternatives

Chapter Two: Energy Efficiency

Introduction

The Energy Debate is the fifty-fourth volume in the **Issues** series. The aim of this series is to offer up-to-date information about important issues in our world.

The Energy Debate looks at the different types of energy and energy efficiency.

The information comes from a wide variety of sources and includes:
Government reports and statistics
Newspaper reports and features
Magazine articles and surveys
Literature from lobby groups
and charitable organisations.

It is hoped that, as you read about the many aspects of the issues explored in this book, you will critically evaluate the information presented. It is important that you decide whether you are being presented with facts or opinions. Does the writer give a biased or an unbiased report? If an opinion is being expressed, do you agree with the writer?

The Energy Debate offers a useful starting-point for those who need convenient access to information about the many issues involved. However, it is only a starting-point. At the back of the book is a list of organisations which you may want to contact for further information.

*****

Energy – a beginner's guide

Information from NATTA – Network for Alternative Technology and Technology Assessment

By Dave Elliott

The generation and use of energy probably has the largest environmental impact of all human activities – from fuel extraction right through to the emissions from power stations and cars. To get to grips with the issues and choices it's useful to have a grasp of the basic science and engineering principles – what is energy, where does it come from, how do we use it? That can equip you with the tools to analyse some of the problems and some of the solutions.

Energy sources

The obvious starting point for our exploration of energy and energy issues is to look at energy sources – where energy comes from.

The energy sources available to mankind fall into two fundamentally differing classes – the renewable sources and the non-renewable sources.

Renewable sources are the naturally occurring, and naturally replenished, energy flows such as sunlight, the winds, the waves and the tides. The winds and waves are actually indirect forms of solar energy – the differential heating of the atmosphere, the land and sea produces winds, and winds moving over the sea produce waves. The sun's heat also drives the hydrological climate system, creating clouds, rain and rivers, whose energy can be tapped in hydroelectric schemes. So that too is, indirectly, a solar source. Tidal energy by contrast is the result of the gravitational interaction of the moon with the seas. So it could be called 'lunar power', although the sun's pull also has an effect.

Sunlight provides energy for plant and animal life, and when this dies and gets buried under geological strata over millennia, it gets converted into fossil materials of various types, coal, oil or gas, depending on the location, duration, temperatures and pressures. These fossil fuel reserves have taken millennia to lay down, as, in effect, stored solar energy, but we have used a large proportion of them in the last hundred years or so: our rate of use far outstrips the rate of regeneration, so in practice they are non-renewable resources.

By contrast, when we use biological material like wood at the same rate as it is produced then that can be thought of as a renewable resource. Like fossil fuels, this is stored solar energy – but it can be continually and relatively quickly replaced.

Finally there is nuclear energy – the energy that can be released when the atomic nucleus of certain materials is disrupted. Reserves of the specific materials needed are limited and are not being renewed: they are part of the planet's initial inheritance, so nuclear power is not a renewable resource.

On a strict interpretation of the term, the same is true of geothermal energy from the heat within the planet. This is the result of heat released due to the radioactive decay of materials deep underground – so you could see geothermal energy as a 'natural' form of nuclear energy. Furthermore, since the sun is a giant fusion reactor, bathing this planet with solar energy, you might say all the energy sources we have discussed, except tidal, are nuclear sources.

• The above information is from NATTA's web site which can be found at technology.open.ac.uk/eeru/natta/

© NATTA

The dinosaur's revenge

Why we can't carry on burning fossil fuel

By Dave Elliott

Most of the energy we use comes from 'fossil' fuels – coal, oil and gas, which we get from deep underground. These fuels were created millions of years ago when the dinosaurs reigned and took millions of years to create – from the remains of plants buried gradually under layers and layers of rock and soil. Some dead dinosaurs no doubt also got involved . . . We've only been raiding the dinosaurs' graveyard, by extracting coal, for a few hundred years, and oil and gas only more recently – but we've already used up a lot of the reserves, especially of oil and gas, which look like they will run out in a few decades.

At one time people thought that running out of these fuels was the main problem – that was the so-called 'energy crisis' of the 1970s. Now it looks like we won't be able to – or shouldn't – use up what remains – because of the effect of burning it on the atmosphere. The problem is what's called the greenhouse effect and it's caused by a gas called carbon dioxide. It's tasteless – it's what's in the bubbles in soft drinks. It's also what you get when you burn fossil fuels – which are basically carbon. Carbon plus oxygen from the air gives you carbon dioxide and heat. That's what burning is all about. Basically we're burning off all the carbon from the fossil material laid down millions of years ago.

The trouble is when you push more and more carbon dioxide gas from burning fossil fuels into the atmosphere, it begins to have an effect on the sunlight that we receive. The gas acts like the glass in a greenhouse, allowing the sun's rays to come in but blocking the escape of heat. So very gradually the whole planet warms up.

The actual average world-wide temperature change is quite small – less than a degree or so in a hundred years. But we are burning more and more, so the rate of temperature rise may increase. And remember the temperature change that caused the ice age was only four degrees or so.

If we persist in burning off the rest of our fossil fuels, we could face another similar change in average temperatures – but this time an increase – and that could mean widespread flooding, more desert areas, crop failures and a lot more. The last couple of years' erratic weather in the UK – hot summers, windy winters – could only be a small sample of what we might expect. And world-wide it could be worse. Millions of people could be affected – around the world – made homeless, losing their food supplies and livelihoods . . .

Not a pleasant thought: the revenge of the dinosaurs if you like . . .

Are there any ways out?

Basically we have to stop burning so much fossil fuel.

We can do that first by stopping wasting so much of the energy we currently have to produce and second by using other types of fuel which don't produce carbon dioxide.

Energy saving first – currently we waste more than half of what we produce, with badly insulated houses, inefficient machines, lighting and cars. A lot can be done to avoid this waste – and to save money.

Second, the alternative sources. Nuclear power was for many people the great hope, at one time – a clever way of twisting the tail of dinosaurs to get power – stealing the dragon's secret if you like. But it's turned out not to be cheap and many people are worried about the risks: again the dinosaurs may get their revenge. Also the reserves of the fuel it needs are not infinite: there's only around fifty

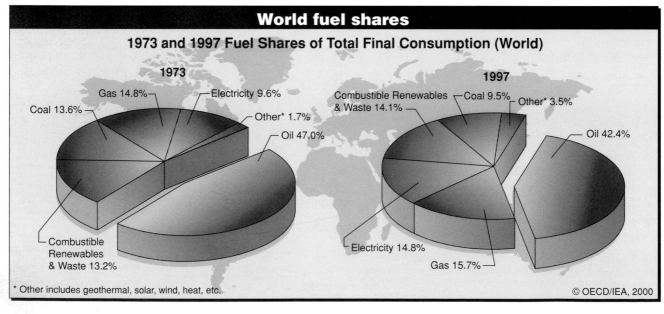

World fuel shares

1973 and 1997 Fuel Shares of Total Final Consumption (World)

1973

- Coal 13.6%
- Gas 14.8%
- Electricity 9.6%
- Other* 1.7%
- Oil 47.0%
- Combustible Renewables & Waste 13.2%

1997

- Combustible Renewables & Waste 14.1%
- Coal 9.5%
- Other* 3.5%
- Oil 42.4%
- Electricity 14.8%
- Gas 15.7%

* Other includes geothermal, solar, wind, heat, etc.

© OECD/IEA, 2000

years' worth of uranium known to be available if we carry on using it as at present – and if we tried to expand nuclear power to take over from coal, we'd use the reserves up even faster. Of course we might be able to find some more uranium and develop ways to use it more efficiently – like the so called fast breeder reactor. But all that does is put off the day when we have to find a long-term, reliable alternative to raiding the dinosaurs' lair. Something which will last.

In the end the only real alternatives are the world's natural energy sources – wind, wave, tidal and solar power. These will continue to be available as long as the planet exists and tapping into them does not use them up. They are naturally replenished – so they are called 'renewables'.

We already get about 20% of the world's electricity very cheaply from hydro-electric dams, but eventually we could supply about the same from each of the other renewables: enough for all we need from a mixture of wind, tidal, wave, and solar powered systems, without producing any carbon dioxide or any other pollutants.

Of course no technology can be entirely without impact – windmills may be thought to intrude on the landscape for example, and big tidal barrages across estuaries will obviously have some local impacts on wildlife. But then the greenhouse effect – or a major nuclear accident – would have much more dramatic impacts. So it's a matter of choice – and renewables are increasingly looking like the cheapest option. Windmills, under some conditions, for example, can generate electricity at half the cost of conventional power plants – and there are now thousands of them in use around the world. These are not primitive low-tech devices, but the very latest in advanced technology – as in the US windfarms.

Britain is very well placed to develop many of the renewables – we have amongst the world's best wind, wave and tidal sites. And the OU is doing its bit to help develop some of them – for example the Open University Energy and Environment Research Unit has a major wind power project and is looking at biofuels and solar energy. We're also looking carefully at the problems of renewables – like their environmental impact. But the message that's emerging is that, given careful design and siting, renewables are very well suited to the UK. So, maybe, we will soon be able to leave the dinosaurs and their graveyard in peace . . .

• The above analysis is very much my own, and should not therefore be taken, necessarily, to reflect the views of the Open University. My use of the 'dinosaur' concept is somewhat geologically light-hearted.

For further information on renewable energy contact NATTA, the independent national Network for Alternative Technology and Technology Assessment c/o Energy and Environment Research Unit, Open University, Milton Keynes, Bucks, MK7 6AA. NATTA produces a bi-monthly Newsletter *Renew* (available on subscription) and has a wide range of reports available.   © *NATTA*

Energy consumption

Information from the Environment Agency

The UK uses fossil fuels in the form of coal, oil, and natural gas, plus nuclear power, as primary sources of energy. Of these fuels, some natural gas is used directly by the consumer but the majority has to be converted into other forms of energy. Crude oil is refined into a range of petroleum products; oil and gas are used in power stations to generate electricity, as is coal. Nuclear power stations use uranium to generate electricity via controlled nuclear fission.

Pressures on the environment arise from the methods used in extracting the primary sources of fuel, from the methods used in converting them into other forms of energy, and from the use of that energy. The Environment Agency has specific responsibilities in relation to the regulation of discharges to the environment from a number of these processes, including refineries, power stations and nuclear power plants, under Integrated Pollution Control (Environmental Protection Act 1990).

Cold weather in 1996 contributed to the UK consuming a

record level of energy. The 1997 yearly consumption, however, dropped back by 3% from this peak figure. On the whole, the total quantities of primary fuels used, expressed as million tonnes of oil equivalent, have not changed greatly in recent years for a number of reasons, but with improved energy efficiency measures playing a large part. The relative use of different primary fuels has however changed, with an increase in the use of natural gas in particular, and a decrease in the use of coal.

Renewable energy sources contribute less than 1% of primary energy consumption in the UK. After a marked increase in 1994, use of renewable sources has largely levelled out, although there was an increase of approximately 10% between 1996 and 1997. The largest renewable source is biofuel (such as wood, straw, municipal waste and sewage sludge).

Both oil and gas are produced primarily from offshore sites. Some oil enters the environment as a result of the disposal of spent drilling cuttings and from the discharges of contaminated water. Oil refineries may also discharge some oil as waste. Leakages in the systems to produce and distribute gas release methane into the atmosphere. Coal mining also results in the release of methane, and can create problems in relation to the water which has to be pumped from working mines, or is permitted to flow from abandoned mines. Large quantities of mining spoil are also produced, which need to be carefully managed. Nuclear power creates radioactive wastes, which require safe and long-term disposal.

The principal environmental impact from the combustion of fossil fuels is that of releases of gases to the atmosphere. The burning of coal is estimated to account for about 25% of the carbon dioxide released into the atmosphere each year by the UK, the vast majority via power stations. The burning of gas and oil is

The UK is estimated to contribute about 1% of the global man-made releases of methane to the atmosphere

estimated to account for about 35% each. Carbon dioxide is one of the 'greenhouse gases'; it exists naturally, but is also one of the gases which is subject to targets for control because it can contribute to what is known as an enhanced greenhouse effect, and thus may contribute to an increase in the earth's surface temperature. The UK contributes about 2% of the total man-made releases of carbon dioxide to the atmosphere. It aims to return the rate of emissions to the 1990 level by the year 2000 under the 1994 Framework Convention on the Atmosphere (Climate Treaty).

The production of coal also results in about 9% of the methane – another 'greenhouse gas' – released to the atmosphere each year in the UK, and about the same amount arises from natural gas production

and distribution. The UK is estimated to contribute about 1% of the global man-made releases of methane to the atmosphere.

The burning of fossil fuels also releases other gases into the atmosphere, particularly sulphur dioxide and oxides of nitrogen, plus black smoke. Of these, nitrous oxide is also a 'greenhouse gas', but the other emissions also give rise to air quality problems.

The largest consumers of energy are transport (34%) and the domestic sector (28%), slightly less is used by industry (24%).

The most recent information on energy production, consumption and its effects is contained in the Department of Trade and Industry's *Digest of UK Energy Statistics 1998*. An Environment Agency report on *Oil and Gas in the Environment* is available from the Stationery Office and a summary is available from Agency Offices.

• The above information is from the Environment Agency web site which can be found at www.environment-agency.gov.uk

© 2000 Environment Agency

Energy consumption in the UK

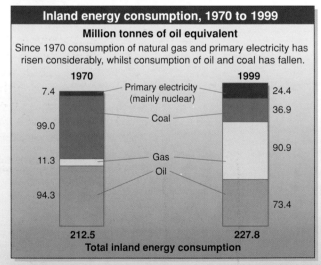

Inland energy consumption, 1970 to 1999

Million tonnes of oil equivalent

Since 1970 consumption of natural gas and primary electricity has risen considerably, whilst consumption of oil and coal has fallen.

1970
- Primary electricity (mainly nuclear): 7.4
- Coal: 99.0
- Gas: 11.3
- Oil: 94.3
- **Total: 212.5**

1999
- Primary electricity (mainly nuclear): 24.4
- Coal: 36.9
- Gas: 90.9
- Oil: 73.4
- **Total: 227.8**

Total inland energy consumption

Since 1970 energy consumption by individual sectors has changed substantially: there have been rises of 90% for transport, 25% for the domestic sector and 15.5% for the service sector.

Renewable energy sources

Total use of renewables	Thousand tonnes of oil equivalent			
	1990	1997	1998	1999
Active solar	6.4	9.0	9.4	10.0
Onshore wind	0.8	57.3	75.4	77.2
Hydro	447.7	358.5	450.3	460.1
Landfill gas	79.8	316.6	402.4	572.0
Sewage sludge digestion	138.2	191.9	180.6	188.8
Wood	174.1	710.3	710.3	710.3
Straw	71.7	71.7	71.7	71.7
Municipal solid waste	160.0	424.2	574.0	580.2
Other biofuels	24.0	189.9	198.2	241.7
Total	**1,102.7**	**2,329.4**	**2,672.3**	**2,912.0**

Final energy consumption, 1999

Million tonnes of oil equivalent

	Industry	Domestic	Transport	Services	Total
Coal & manufactured fuels	3.5	2.5	-	0.2	6.3
Gas	15.9	30.6	-	10.4	56.9
Oil	6.1	3.2	53.0	2.7	65.1
Electricity	9.1	9.5	0.7	8.0	27.3
Total	**35.2**	**46.1**	**53.7**	**21.5**	**156.5**

Source: Department of Trade and Industry (DTI). © Crown Copyright

Costly energy

Information from Friends of the Earth

FRIENDS *of the*
earth
for the planet **for people**

The problem

We use energy in almost everything we do: for heating our homes, cooking our meals and powering our cars. But the major source of this energy is largely to blame for the climate changes we are now experiencing.

When we burn fossil fuel (oil, coal, natural gas, petrol and diesel) for energy, carbon dioxide is released. And, along with other greenhouse gases, carbon dioxide traps the sun's heat in the atmosphere, leading to global warming and climate change.

The solution

Friends of the Earth believes we can meet our energy needs without damaging the health of our planet, through investing in green energy and energy efficiency – something we can all buy into. And using the Earth's resources more efficiently and effectively has got to be good for the planet, for us, and for our future.

Fossil fuels

Our use of fossil fuels doesn't just cause climate change; acid rain and oil spills continue to threaten habitats and wildlife due to our over-reliance on this polluting energy source.

Lakes and forests across Europe are still regularly damaged by acid rain. And the *Exxon Valdez* and *Sea Empress* accidents in 1989 and 1997 clearly show that the threat of oil spills from tanker transportation is ever present, causing serious harm to local marine life.

Vested interests

To move away from traditional fossil fuel energy production, government must put pressure on business to introduce energy-efficient measures and increase investment in renewable energy. But vested interests of the fossil fuel companies continue to thwart attempts to get government and industry to take the climate threat seriously.

The 'Global Climate Coalition', formed by the fossil fuel companies to protect their profits, questions the existence of climate change and lobbies against any action taken to prevent further change. Household names such as Esso, Vauxhall and Texaco have all stood in the way of progress. Meanwhile other companies, such as BP and Shell, recognise where their future profits lie and are investing in new technologies, such as less polluting fuels and renewable energy.

Nuclear power – a not-so-clean alternative

Some people champion nuclear power as a solution to reducing carbon dioxide emissions. Friends of the Earth disagrees and has campaigned tirelessly against nuclear power since the 1970s.

A safe option?

The 1986 explosion at Chernobyl and the 1999 nuclear scare in Tokyo show that nuclear power stations can be catastrophically dangerous and that the threat of nuclear accidents is still very real. No amount of radiation is safe and yet Sellafield and many other nuclear power sites around the UK are still legally allowed to release radioactive waste into the sky and sea.

The real cost

Nuclear power is expensive – subsidised to the tune of £1 billion a year in the 1990s. It is officially estimated that by 2100 at least £40 billion will need to be spent on waste management costs alone. The amount spent on developing pollution-free technologies such as solar power has been a small fraction of this.

The problem of waste

There is no solution to the problem of nuclear waste. Scientists have failed to come up with an effective way of disposing of it. In 1995 Friends of the Earth and other groups successfully opposed the planned nuclear waste dump at Sellafield. The plan was to build a deep disposal site making the waste almost impossible to monitor and recover if there were any problems. Scientific evidence presented by Friends of the Earth and others persuaded the then secretary of state John Gummer to refuse planning permission for the dump.

© Friends of the Earth

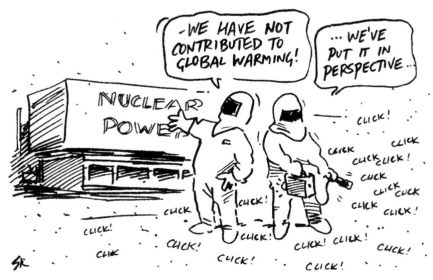

Why nuclear energy has to be part of the solution

By Peter Hollins.
First published in Energy World Magazine

The World Energy Council has predicted that our planet will consume 75% more electricity in 2020 than it does today – and further estimates that global demand will treble by 2050. The case for sustainable development has never been more pressing.

The challenge that lies ahead is clear. How can we supply the growing demand for electricity while, at the same time, minimising any adverse impact on the environment for future generations and maintaining a stable, diverse energy mix?

Along with my colleagues in the nuclear energy industry, I firmly believe that the industry should be deployed as a major component of national and international strategies to mitigate climate change. Nuclear energy is very much part of the solution. But why?

Nuclear energy is both large scale (base-load) and carbon-free. Nuclear stations emit only negligible amounts of carbon dioxide (CO_2) and the other greenhouses gases that scientists believe are responsible for global warming.

But you don't have to take my word for it – the figures speak for themselves.

British Energy's eight, modern nuclear power stations provided just over a fifth of the UK's electricity in the year ending March 31st 1998, the 21% market share making the company the country's largest generator. In total, nearly 30% of the UK's electricity is generated by nuclear fission.

Our 66.7TWh (terawatt hours) effectively avoided the release of 51 million tonnes of CO_2 (compared with the current fossil-fuel mix) into the atmosphere. To put this in context, it is equivalent to removing over 70% of all cars from the roads in the UK.

In Europe, nuclear is the largest single fuel source, accounting for 34% of the energy mix, and on a global scale, the nuclear component is 17%. This adds up to the avoidance of many million tonnes of CO_2 – a fact that I am sure is not widely appreciated.

Globally, there will obviously be a need for energy strategies that are long-term, secure, environmentally acceptable and able to meet predicted needs – and help the developed world meet the legally-binding reduction targets agreed at the Kyoto climate change conference.

The Kyoto Protocol sets targets based on 1990 levels for cuts in emissions by 2008-2012 for each of six identified greenhouse gases. The British Government took a lead at both the Rio 'Earth Summit' and at Kyoto last December in undertaking to reduce the UK's 1990 levels of greenhouse gas emissions by 20% by 2010. The performance of the UK's nuclear stations will be an important factor in enabling the UK to meet its Rio commitment – one of the few countries that looks likely to do so.

Maintaining a significant nuclear component in the UK fuel mix in the medium to long term is the only realistic option if Government's reduction targets are to be met. Although some reductions could be delivered by promoting the more efficient use of energy and by providing further incentives for investment in renewables, these measures are unlikely to be sufficient on their own.

A cross-party Select Committee agrees: 'Without a significant component of nuclear power generation in the plant mix, achievement – or maintenance – of a 20% CO_2 reduction on the 1990 level in the period after 2010 appears doubtful' reported the House of Commons Trade and Industry Committee on energy policy in June.

The Committee's conclusions on the prospect of new build are encouraging and will help stimulate debate on the subject. Although there is no current commercial case to build new nuclear plant in Britain to replace existing stations when they reach the end of their operating lifetimes, the Committee accepted that the repercussions of Kyoto would 'lead to the re-opening of the

Electricity supplied by fuel type

The mix of fuels used to generate electricity continues to evolve. In 1999 gas supplied more electricity than coal for the first time.

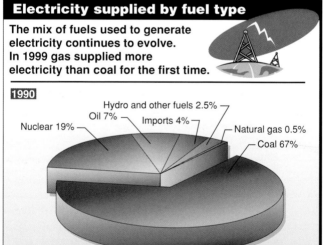

1990

- Nuclear 19%
- Oil 7%
- Hydro and other fuels 2.5%
- Imports 4%
- Natural gas 0.5%
- Coal 67%

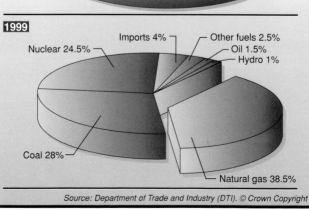

1999

- Nuclear 24.5%
- Imports 4%
- Other fuels 2.5%
- Oil 1.5%
- Hydro 1%
- Coal 28%
- Natural gas 38.5%

Source: Department of Trade and Industry (DTI). © Crown Copyright

question as to whether new nuclear generation capacity should be envisaged'.

Given the right fiscal and legislative environment, the nuclear generating industry can continue to play a crucial role in reducing CO_2 emissions while, at the same time, providing the security of a balanced energy mix. It can't be if – it has to be when.

My view that new nuclear power capacity may ultimately be required to help achieve that critical balance between environmental and economic objectives, is echoed in the Select Committee's 'warning' to Government that: 'the question of new nuclear build cannot and must not be ducked any longer. We recommend that a formal presumption be made now for purposes of

long-term planning that new nuclear plant may be required in the course of the next two decades.'

If the aspirations of Rio and Kyoto are to become reality, then new nuclear capacity will be an issue none of us can afford to duck.

• The above is an extract from British Energy's web site which can be found at www.british-energy.com

Energy for life

Information from British Nuclear Fuels (BNFL)

It is through the scientific and technological achievements of men and women since the Industrial Revolution that our natural energy resources have been developed to provide us with an abundance of food and an amazing variety of buildings, consumer goods, communications, industrial processes and transport. Whether we like it or not, civilisation, as we know it, could not continue without a vast and sophisticated technology, bringing power to the people, hour after hour, year in, year out.

Much of the energy we have used in our developing world has come from fossil fuels such as coal, oil and gas. These fuels have enabled us to provide lighting and heating in our homes, offices and factories, and transport to school, work and leisure. Today, we are so used to the benefits of these services that power cuts and shortages can have an alarming effect on our personal lives, and devastating effects on our industrial and commercial output.

And what of the future?

Although fossil fuels such as coal, oil and gas will service our needs for some considerable time to come, they are not inexhaustible and are not without environmental impacts. They will, eventually, be used up or become too expensive as supplies run out. Increasing population growth and increased energy usage in the developing countries will probably accelerate this process. The impact of global warming upon fossil fuel

use is also uncertain. But, unfortunately, there is every reason to believe that our demand for electricity will continue to grow. What, then, can be done?

Renewable energy sources for producing electricity, such as wind, water and the sun are growing in use, but their contribution to our total requirements is still small. Solar cells, generating electricity from the sun, are expensive, and tidal barrages are both expensive and at an early stage of technological development. Within the UK, there is little prospect of developing more hydropower because of the shortage of suitable water tracts. The use of wind power is increasing but it is unreliable because of fluctuating wind currents, and the technology to harness wave power is still in its infancy. As technology advances, renewables are likely to become more important in our mixture of energy options. However, it is unlikely, even in the most optimistic forecasts, that they will totally replace conventional electricity sources for at least a generation or perhaps even longer.

So where do we turn in order to ensure our future electricity needs?

Energy options
Nuclear power now supplies approximately 24.5% of electricity in the UK, and is a source which can be used to meet increased demand. It has added bonuses. By using nuclear power, we currently save over 20 million tonnes of coal each year, which will help our fossil fuels last longer, and free them as a future valuable raw material for chemicals, fertilisers and plastics. In addition, nuclear power stations do not produce the gases which contribute to global warming and acid rain.

Electricity sources
Coal
The major fuel used to generate electricity in the UK. Estimates suggest that the world's reserves of coal will last for about 250 years. Burning coal in power stations releases carbon dioxide (CO_2) sulphur dioxide (SO_2) and oxides of nitrogen into the atmosphere. These contribute to global warming and acid rain.

Gas
An important, and growing, fuel source for generating electricity in the UK. Gas-fired power stations can be very efficient. However, natural gas (methane) also contributes to global warming when it escapes into the atmosphere.

Oil
An important fuel source in generating electricity in the UK. But it is important to remember that oil has

many other uses, and estimates suggest that the world's reserves of oil may last for only another 40 years or so.

Nuclear power

Currently providing about 24.5% of the UK's electricity supply, with potential to contribute more (although this may decrease if no new nuclear power stations are brought on line in the future). Nuclear fuel can be recycled and does not produce greenhouse gases, but the waste must be safely managed.

Hydro

Currently making a useful contribution to electricity generation in Scotland. The best sites in the UK for large dams and reservoirs have already been used, so further potential seems limited.

Wind

Wind farms are becoming an increasingly common sight in the UK. Wind power has potential for the future, although fluctuating wind currents may make it unreliable and the turbines can be unsightly.

Tidal

Capturing the energy of the tides involves building a huge barrier (or 'barrage') across a suitable river estuary. Britain has a number of suitable sites for such a scheme – for example the Mersey or the Severn.

Wave

Several devices have been proposed to use the up-and-down motion of waves to generate electricity. However, the wild conditions which are often experienced at sea make the engineering and anchoring of wave power devices extremely difficult.

Solar

Particularly appropriate in those parts of the world where direct sunlight can produce an electric current by means of a solar cell. One option for the UK is to make sure that new buildings make the most of the sun – for example, by having large, south-facing windows ('passive solar heating').

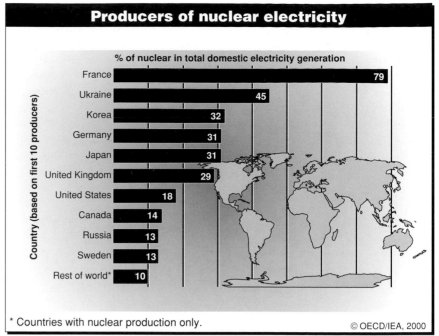

Producers of nuclear electricity

% of nuclear in total domestic electricity generation

Country (based on first 10 producers)

Country	%
France	79
Ukraine	45
Korea	32
Germany	31
Japan	31
United Kingdom	29
United States	18
Canada	14
Russia	13
Sweden	13
Rest of world*	10

* Countries with nuclear production only.

© OECD/IEA, 2000

For today and tomorrow

Although nuclear fuel operates in a reactor for several years, it eventually begins to function less efficiently and needs to be replaced by new fuel. The reprocessing of irradiated (used) nuclear fuel and the managing of waste products has been undertaken at Sellafield in Cumbria for over 30 years. The site has established itself as a world leader in this high technology field.

One of the earliest developments at Sellafield was the Windscale piles used solely for producing weapons materials. The fire in one of the piles in 1957 resulted in their closure and in a complete reorganisation of the nuclear safety programme in Britain, and led directly to the setting up of the Nuclear Installations Inspectorate and to guidelines on many health and safety controls.

Rules and regulations

BNFL's operational sites are licensed under the Nuclear Installations Act

---

The problem facing us today is to find a way of satisfying this growing need for energy while reducing the pollution associated with conventional forms of energy

---

and are subject to inspection by the Nuclear Installations Inspectorate. Each site licence contains a substantial number of requirements and conditions designed to safeguard workers and the public.

All working practices with radio-active materials are strictly controlled. Many operations are carried out in cells, completely shielded with concrete or lead, and using remotely controlled equipment. Extensive ventilation and filtration systems are used and the working area is constantly monitored in a variety of ways.

BNFL also monitors the environment around its sites. Thousands of samples are collected and analysed each year, including milk, seafoods, air and water. In recent years, BNFL has spent nearly £1 billion designing and building plants to reduce radio-active waste discharges to the Irish Sea.

Worldwide policy

The explosion at the Chernobyl nuclear power station in the Ukraine in 1986 made the public, worldwide and at home, aware of the need for strict checks on safety in the nuclear industry.

BNFL's policy is that nothing is more important than the health and safety of its employees, the general public, and the protection of the environment. Beyond that, everyone in the UK is encouraged to understand more of what is being done by BNFL so that they can understand the international significance of safe and efficient nuclear power systems. The type of reactor used at Chernobyl was thought to be potentially too dangerous by UK experts to be used in our nuclear industry. BNFL believes that a global policy for safety and efficiency is not only desirable, but it is necessary to protect the social and economic interests of the community around its own sites, and the wider world environment.

Today 85% of the average radiation dose of a person living in the UK is from natural sources – such as cosmic radiation, radon gas – which occurs naturally in our atmosphere, or from gamma radiation from the Earth. Less than 0.1% of the average person's radiation dose in the UK comes from the nuclear industry compared with 14% from X-rays and other medical uses.

The greenhouse effect

As the world population grows, so demand for energy increases. The problem facing us today is to find a way of satisfying this growing need for energy while reducing the pollution associated with conventional forms of energy.

A pressing need is to reduce the emission of the gases which are responsible for global warming. There is no single solution, and it is likely that we will continue to rely on a mix of energy sources.

© British Nuclear Fuels plc

Nuclear power

Information from OneWorld

Disaster stories

Most people only hear about nuclear power when it goes badly wrong. Disasters such as Chernobyl (1986), Three Mile Island (1979) or Windscale (1957) raise public fears for a while, yet the media blackout on the thousands of other accidents which have occurred over the past 50 years gives the impression that nuclear power is relatively safe. Full details of all the near-misses might dent public confidence: France's chief safety inspector made headlines when he predicted a one in 20 chance of a major accident in one of the country's ageing reactors before the year 2010.

Radiation risks

Even without the accidents, radiation from nuclear power plants is already a killer. Leukaemia clusters and high incidence of other cancers have revealed the risks of living near nuclear sites, as discharges into air and sea introduce radiation pollution into the atmosphere and the food chain. Workers employed in the nuclear industry – whether in uranium mines or power stations – are at even greater risk, as are any children they may have. Following research into increased levels of child leukaemia around the Sellafield site in north-west England, British Nuclear Fuels suggested that high-risk areas of the plant should not be staffed by men likely to have families.

Waste disposal

Fears of radiation contamination underlie one of the nuclear industry's major unsolved problems: what to do with its waste. Much of the high-level waste which has already been produced in nuclear power generation will remain radioactive for thousands of years, necessitating safe storage for periods well beyond anything the nuclear industry can guarantee. The 1957 explosion at Kyshtym in Russia (the most serious nuclear disaster ever, next to Chernobyl) is only the most extreme example of the dangers involved in storing concentrated nuclear waste.

Reprocessing

Reprocessing nuclear fuel was once heralded as the most efficient way of dealing with nuclear waste, as it takes 'spent' fuel rods and separates out uranium for reuse in power stations and plutonium for use either in 'fast breeder' reactors or – worst of all – in nuclear weapons (for which reprocessing was originally developed). Unfortunately, however, re-

processing actually multiplies the volume of radioactive waste created by at least 160 times. And the nuclear industry's fast breeder hopes were dashed in 1997 when Japan and France followed Britain and the USA in announcing the end of their programmes.

The end of an industry

In view of the many problems and the enormous expense involved in generating nuclear energy, most countries are now turning away from nuclear power. Germany's new government has joined Sweden and the Netherlands in working to phase out their nuclear programmes entirely, while all other Western European countries have rejected plans for any further reactors (except for France, whose programme has been reduced to its lowest level for 25 years). No new reactors have been ordered for 20 years in either the USA or Canada, while in Asia the expected interest in nuclear energy has failed to materialise. Nuclear power cannot offer the clean, cheap alternative to fossil fuels that was once hoped.

• The above information is from one of OneWorld's guides which aim to challenge and inform, questioning assumptions and suggesting alternatives on the subjects that really matter. OneWorld's web site can be found at www.oneworld.org

© OneWorld

New power for Britain

A strategy for a renewable energy industry

- The United Kingdom (UK) has one of the largest renewable resources in Europe, a resource which could meet all our electricity needs many times over. Despite this vast natural resource the UK generates less than 1% of its energy from renewables and languishes at the bottom of the European renewable 'energy league table'.

- Greenpeace believes the UK can meet all its electricity needs by harnessing just three truly 'clean' renewable technologies: wind, solar and wave. Studies have shown that both wind and wave could meet the UK's electricity needs three times over. Solar could provide two-thirds of the UK's electricity.

- The UK Government's failure to exploit this vast natural resource is undermining its competitive advantage in the renewables market. The existing Non Fossil Fuel Obligation (NFFO) has failed to deliver any significant renewable manufacturing capacity for the UK. Instead thousands of jobs have been lost to other countries that are rapidly developing their renewable industries. If and when the UK Government finally does act, it faces the humiliating prospect of becoming a net importer of many technologies that it helped to pioneer.

- Government action on renewables will be essential if real progress is to be made by the UK in cutting carbon dioxide emissions. Left unchecked climate change will cause havoc with ecosystems and financial costs from extreme weather events and the spread of disease will escalate. Evidence from around the world shows these changes are already happening.

- To prevent further climate change we must 'put the lid on fossil fuels' once and for all. The United Nations has stated that a temperature rise of 1°C above pre-industrial levels may lead to extensive ecosystem damage. Taking this figure and the fossil fuel reserves identified by the Intergovernmental Panel on Climate Change, Greenpeace has calculated that globally we can only burn around 225 gigatonnes of carbon – less than a quarter of existing known reserves. Translating this carbon budget into an energy policy means that we have to phase out fossil fuels in the next 30 to 40 years.

- If fossil fuels are to be phased out, a massive renewable energy programme will be needed. 'New Power for Britain' is essential to delivering the UK's Kyoto climate commitments, building a dynamic new industry and creating thousands of much needed jobs. The European Commission has calculated that just doubling the amount of renewables in Europe would create 500,000 to 900,000 new jobs. If the UK is to share in this new job bonanza the Government must commit itself to an ambitious renewable energy programme which harnesses the true potential of the wind, the sun and the waves.

- To exploit the UK's vast renewable resource will require greatly expanding mechanisms like the NFFO. The dramatic decline in research and development into emerging technologies must also be reversed. To help finance this, subsidies from the nuclear and fossil fuel industries should be transferred to a renewable energy programme.

- The UK Government's aim is to provide just 10% of electricity from renewables by 2010. This narrow thinking will not exploit the full potential of the UK's renewable manufacturing industry. A new approach to developing renewable energy is needed to ensure that the UK develops the maximum number of new manufacturing facilities and new jobs.

- Member States in the European Union have set renewable targets not just for 2010 but 2020 and 2030. The UK Government should follow this example and put in place a political process that sets renewable targets beyond 2010. This should lead to a fossil fuel phase out in the next 30 to 40 years.

© Greenpeace

Renewable energy policy for the UK

Information from WWF-UK

The burning of fossil fuels to produce energy has a host of environmental impacts, most notably the production of carbon dioxide which is the main contributor to climate change. Under the Kyoto Protocol the UK government has a commitment to reduce the emissions of a basket of greenhouse gases, including carbon dioxide, by 12.5% of the 1990 level by 2008-2012. In addition the UK has a domestic target to reduce carbon dioxide emissions by 20 per cent of the 1990 level by 2010.

Given that the production and use of energy is responsible for some two-thirds of the UK's carbon dioxide emissions, 30 per cent from electricity generation alone, it is clear that a move towards less carbon intensive technologies such as renewables, is essential if the UK is to meet its greenhouse gas emission targets. Reducing the use of fossil fuels will also have other environmental benefits such as improving air quality and reducing the impact caused by extracting the fuels. In addition, the introduction of renewable technologies can bring economic benefits in the form of jobs and industrial activity.

WWF is committed to promoting renewable energy technologies that can replace fossil fuels and thus reduce the environmental impact caused by energy production. However WWF recognises that renewables are not necessarily environmentally benign and they can have some local impacts. These should be balanced with the benefits in terms of emissions. Projects should be sited sensitively and in areas where they will cause least damage to the environment.

WWF believes that there must be appropriate support mechanisms in place to ensure that renewables make up an increasing amount of the UK's electricity supply. This should include an obligation on all suppliers of electricity to ensure that they supply an increasing amount of their electricity from renewable sources. There also needs to be a system of support to ensure that the less mature – and more expensive – renewable technologies are able to compete in the wholesale electricity market.

In addition, the planning problems that are a barrier to the development of renewable technologies must be addressed. This should include an assessment of the environmental impact of renewable projects applying for government support and a system of local planning where planners identify within their structure plans sites where renewable developments would be accepted.

There are a variety of different renewable technologies available, WWF's views as to the suitability of each technology are outlined below:

Energy from Waste (industrial and domestic)
WWF does not consider this to be a renewable technology.

Biomass
An energy plantation could benefit the local area and improve land previously used for farming, but can cause significant damage to an area already rich in biodiversity. The use of animal waste, particularly for anaerobic digestion, could be hampered by animal welfare concerns in that the ideal sources of waste are often from intensively farmed animals.

Small-Scale Hydro
The best sites for these schemes are often areas of ecological significance and local amenity. Any proposals would need to be carefully examined in terms of their effects on aquatic life.

Photovoltaics
There is considerable scope for solar cells to be integrated into domestic and industrial building developments, although the high cost of their production may be a problem.

Tidal Power
Due to the high environmental impact plus the associated financial costs, these schemes should not be developed.

Wind Power
WWF supports the development of wind energy, with careful consideration of each proposal. We believe there are many misconceptions about the impact of wind turbines, most of which can be addressed and alleviated through local consultation and accurate information dissemination. The impacts of offshore wind turbines on the marine environment must be examined fully.

Wave Power
There must be further investigation into the full impacts of this technology before WWF can give full support.

Marine Currents
This is a new technology which may contribute to the overall supply of renewable energy, but its full impacts must be examined before WWF can give it full support.

Renewable energy

Information from NEF Renewables – The National Energy Foundation

A large amount of the energy we buy today comes from fossil fuel and nuclear power stations. During the burning of these fossil fuels, emissions are released into the atmosphere which impact upon our environment. These include carbon and sulphur dioxides which contribute to climate change and acid rain. Both fossil and nuclear fuels depend on limited resources. There are serious doubts surrounding the safety of nuclear technology, and how to dispose of the radioactive waste products. Over the last twenty years there have been major steps in the development of renewable energy technology for both industry and domestic use. This has been encouraged partly because of concerns about the environment but also to achieve better security of supply.

Renewables

It is increasingly possible for consumers to invest in renewable energy by purchasing 'green electricity'. This has been made possible by the deregulation of the electricity industry. Now consumers can choose to buy electricity from a range of suppliers, many of which now offer a green tariff.

Passive solar

The use of passive solar design is possibly the simplest form of solar energy. Many buildings today are designed to utilise the energy of the sun as efficiently as possible. The location and orientation of the building are all key factors in optimising passive solar design.

Solar water heating

Solar panels are typically roof mounted. They work by absorbing solar radiation (the sun's energy) to heat water. Solar water heating (SWH) panels are the most commonly used form of solar energy currently used today. A typical installed system will provide 50-70% of hot water needs over the year.

Did you know . . . ?

At present over 2% of electricity produced in the UK comes from a renewable source. By the year 2005 the Government's target is to exceed 5% and by 2010, 10%. Various predictions suggest we will achieve 50% by the year 2050.

Photovoltaic (solar electric)

Solar electric technology is simply the conversion of solar radiation into electricity.

The variety of applications for solar electric are numerous. Photovoltaic (PV) cells are used in simple applications e.g. calculators and watches and also for larger applications. Large PV systems can be integrated into buildings to generate electricity for export to the National Grid.

Wind energy

People have used the power of the wind for many years to produce mechanical power for milling grain and pumping water. In recent times wind turbine technology has enabled us to harness wind to generate electricity. This renewable source of energy has great potential in both onshore and offshore wind farms.

Wind power is one of the cleanest and safest of all the renewable commercial methods of generating electricity. The UK has the largest wind resource in the whole of Europe.

Biomass energy

Today, fast-growing trees like willow and poplar can be used as commercial energy crops to meet local heating needs, or used in power stations to generate electricity. These energy crops offer a means of developing a renewable source in many agricultural areas of the country, supplying power and creating employment. Wastes from agricultural and forestry operations can also be used in this way.

Hydropower

The energy potential of moving water has been harnessed for thousands of years, originally using water wheels to drive mills and machinery. Hydropower currently produces 2% of the UK electricity needs. Whilst most of this comes from large dam projects installed many years ago, there is still an untapped small hydropower potential in certain parts of the UK.

● The above is an extract from NEF Renewables' web site which can be found at www.greenenergy.org.uk

Go with the flow

Water power is one of the oldest established means of harnessing energy and its potential remains limitless

Harnessing water power was one of the great stimulators of the Industrial Revolution and today renewable water power generates up to 20% of the world's electricity without causing emissions or pollution. Its potential to help transform how our energy is generated is vast but the technology has barely been allowed to develop. Today there are three main technologies harnessing water power: wave, tidal and hydro.

The year 2000 saw the 200th anniversary of the first patent on a wave energy device, by two Frenchmen. What is extraordinary is that so little work has been done exploiting the vast natural energy of the sea since 1800. The waters around Scotland are conservatively thought able to provide all the UK with its energy, but despite an early lead, the technology is not favoured by the British government and wave power remains the Cinderella of renewable energy.

Wave devices are many and various, ranging from barges and oscillating columns, to pendulums, buoys and devices installed on land. None, however, have been successfully commercialised. But Islay, off the Scottish coast, is becoming the world capital of wave energy, having been the location for a small experimental plant for the last five years.

Sweden, Norway and Japan presently lead the world race to build successful devices that can produce electricity competitively. As ever, it needs money and a political commitment. Despite few returns so far, there are good long-term prospects for development of commercial wave-power plants.

Tidal power stations are already being used in Canada, France, Russia and China, but tidal power stations are expensive and have environmental problems because they destroy homes to many birds, fish and other animals.

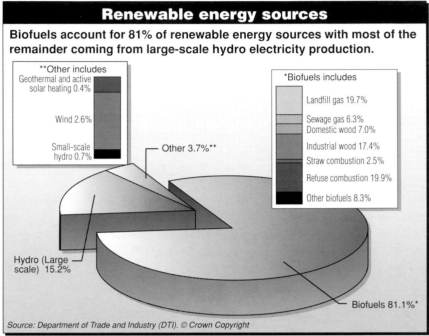

Renewable energy sources

Biofuels account for 81% of renewable energy sources with most of the remainder coming from large-scale hydro electricity production.

**Other includes
Geothermal and active solar heating 0.4%
Wind 2.6%
Small-scale hydro 0.7%

Other 3.7%**

*Biofuels includes
Landfill gas 19.7%
Sewage gas 6.3%
Domestic wood 7.0%
Industrial wood 17.4%
Straw combustion 2.5%
Refuse combustion 19.9%
Other biofuels 8.3%

Hydro (Large scale) 15.2%

Biofuels 81.1%*

Source: Department of Trade and Industry (DTI). © Crown Copyright

Small hydropower (SHP) harnesses water from rivers or small dams to drive turbines. It is probably the most cost-effective, proven and reliable method of harvesting water energy. There are several hundred of these dotted around Britain, designed to provide energy for places far from national grids, but new schemes are often fiercely opposed by fishers, tourist authorities and locals.

The waters around Scotland are conservatively thought able to provide all the UK with its energy

---

Though the power of large dams is vast, here in Britain the era of big dam-building is mostly over, even though the water companies are keen to build new ones to provide water and electricity for the relatively dry and energy-guzzling south and east of England.

Worldwide the picture is different. Some 45,000 large dams have been built in the last 50 years and electricity from them accounts for more than half of all electricity in 66 countries. Last year more than 1,700 new dams were being constructed to provide new, renewable energy to many millions in developing countries.

The emphasis on sustainable development in the past decade has thrown the spotlight on these large infrastructural projects, their social effects and their real economic, environmental and social costs. Their construction often involves the enforced move of hundreds of thousands of people, they may have a short life because they are liable to silt up within a generation, the people affected are seldom consulted and they can impose a system of intensive agriculture that is unwelcome.

More sensitive alternatives are now being widely considered and the growth of wind and solar power should go a long way to changing opinions. But a global big dam industry dominated by a few large construction companies is entrenched and the pressures on politicians to come up with mega-projects is intense.

National wind power

There is now clear evidence that global warming and climate change are a reality, and will have major adverse effects on sea levels, water supply and agriculture world-wide in the coming decades. One of the major causes of global warming is the emission of large volumes of the gas carbon dioxide, resulting from, amongst other things, the generation of electricity.

In the UK, all political parties are committed to the principle of 'sustain-able development'. This is defined as 'development that meets the needs of the present without compromising the ability of future generations to meet their own needs'. The Government is working towards a target of providing 10% of UK electricity supplies from renewable sources by 2010. The recent report by the Royal Commission on Environmental Pollution (*Twenty-second Report. Energy – The Changing Climate*, June 2000), confirms the widely acknowledged fact that wind energy, both onshore and offshore, will play an important part in meeting this target.

The UK has the best wind resource in Europe, to the extent that wind farms could provide up to 20% of Britain's electricity demand using onshore wind energy. The offshore wind resource is also very large and demonstration offshore wind farms are being planned.

The Government is committed to a strong drive to develop wind power and other renewable tech-nologies. It continues to support current contracts called the Non-Fossil Fuel Obligation (NFFO) and the Scottish Renewable Obligation (SRO), but is looking to introduce a market based support mechanism for renewables. This would place an obligation on electricity suppliers to buy an increasing propor-tion of electricity from renewable energy sources.

Developments in wind turbine technology have meant that costs have already fallen to the point where wind energy is now cheaper than nuclear and new coal, and the unit price is approaching those for conventional sources of electricity generation.

Wind energy is a growing business. By mid 2000 a total capacity of over 350MW had already been installed in the UK, meeting the average electricity needs of over 200,000 homes. World-wide the installed wind turbine capacity is growing rapidly and now exceeds 14,000MW, with over 9,000MW in Europe.

Harnessing the power of the wind is not a new concept. Wind power has been in use for thousands of years and at the end of the 18th century there were an estimated 10,000 windmills in operation across the length and breadth of Britain.

As the established leader of this new and rapidly expanding industry, National Wind Power's policy is to pioneer, promote and develop wind farm projects which take into account both the needs of the local people and the environment, whilst helping to meet our energy require-ments in a clean and sustainable way.

© *National Wind Power*

Electricity – the facts

Information from National Wind Power

When we switch on a light, boil the kettle or turn on the tele-vision, it is easy to take electricity for granted, to the extent that we now regard it as a necessity. Nearly all of the 20 million or so homes in Britain are connected to the electricity supply grid and consume around a third of all the electricity generated; the remainder is used by industry and commerce.

Electricity is currently produced in a number of ways; approximately two-thirds is generated by burning fossil fuels like coal, oil and gas. These fuels are not only a limited resource but they also release emissions into the atmosphere which contribute to the problems of climate change, acid rain and global warming. Nuclear power now accounts for around a quarter of UK generation although the costs and the long-term hazards associated with the decommissioning of nuclear plants and the handling of radioactive waste are well known.

The rest of our electricity is generated from renewable means such as hydro (water), wind and gas from landfill sites.

By reducing our consumption of electricity we can help reduce the impacts on the environment which result from its production. However, the need will remain to produce electricity in large quantities, so a move must be made towards generating it in sustainable ways that do not pollute our environment.

As technology advances, so new improved wind turbines have evolved over the years. Modern wind turbines or three bladed rotors of around 40 metres in diameter, supported on tubular steel towers up to 50 metres high. When the wind blows, the blades turn at a constant speed of approximately 30 revolutions per minute, driving a gearbox and then a generator which feeds its electrical output to the electricity grid for delivery to consumers.

A well-sited wind farm of about twenty turbines has an average output sufficient to meet the electricity needs of about 15,000 homes. This clean output results in a reduction in the amount of coal which has to be burnt in older fossil fuelled power stations, such that it offsets the emission of about 45,000 tonnes of carbon dioxide (the main greenhouse gas) and 600 tonnes of acid rain gases every year.

• The above is an extract from the National Wind Power web site which can be found at www.natwindpower.co.uk © *National Wind Power*

British wind energy

Frequently asked questions

THE BRITISH
WIND ENERGY
ASSOCIATION

Here are some of the most commonly asked questions about wind energy. The answers are generally short, and often refer to more detailed explanations given elsewhere.

Wind energy and environmental impact

Are wind turbines noisy?
Wind turbines are not noisy. It is possible to stand underneath a turbine and hold a conversation without having to raise your voice. When it is very windy, the noise of the wind masks the noise made by wind turbines.

Why don't they make turbines that look like old-fashioned windmills?
The old-fashioned windmill is viewed with nostalgia, and some people prefer the look of them to that of their modern counterparts. Just because wind turbines are modern, it does not mean that they are less aesthetically pleasing.

A modern wind turbine is simply an improved windmill. Every aspect of their design has been optimised, and they are hundreds of times more efficient than an old-fashioned windmill. To make them look more old-fashioned would result in much more expensive electricity.

Why don't we put all the wind turbines out to sea?
It is more expensive to have offshore wind farms, although the price is coming down. However, the stronger winds generally found at sea mean that more electricity can be generated. Here in the UK, we are lucky enough to have good winds both on and offshore, and installation of the first offshore turbines began in April 2000. Further develop-ment of the offshore wind energy industry in the UK is likely, with recent suggestions that as much as 10% of the total UK electricity demand could easily be met by offshore wind turbines.

Do wind turbines frighten livestock?
Wind farming is popular with farmers, because their land can continue to be used for growing crops or grazing livestock. Sheep, cows and horses are not disturbed by wind turbines.

The first wind farm built in the UK, Delabole, has a stud farm and riding school, and the farmer, Peter Edwards, often rides around the wind farm on his horse.

How long does it take for a turbine to 'pay back' the electricity used to manufacture it?
The comparison of energy used in manufacture with the energy produced by a power station is known as the 'energy balance'. It can be expressed in terms of energy 'pay back' time, i.e. as the time needed to

generate the equivalent amount of energy used in manufacturing the wind turbine or power station.

The average wind farm in the UK will pay back the energy used in its manufacture within three to five months, and over its lifetime a wind turbine will produce over 30 times more energy than was used in its manufacture. This compares favourably with coal or nuclear power stations, which deliver only a third of the total energy used in construction and fuel supply. So if fuel is included in the calculation, fossil fuel or nuclear power stations never achieve an energy pay back.

Public opinion

How popular is wind energy?
Wind energy is one of the most popular energy technologies. Opinion surveys regularly show that just over eight out of ten people are in favour of wind energy, and less than one in ten (around 5%) are against it. The rest are undecided.

How safe is wind energy?
Wind energy is one of the safest energy technologies. No member of the public has ever been injured by wind energy or wind turbines anywhere in the world, despite the fact that there are now around 35,000 operational wind turbines. Paul Gipe wrote this in his book *Wind Power Comes of Age* in 1996 and it remains true to this day.

Does wind farming affect tourism?
There is no evidence to suggest that wind farms detract tourists, indeed many wind farms are themselves tourist attractions.

What is Country Guardian?
The Country Guardian is an organisation which campaigns against the development of wind energy. They oppose all wind farm and wind turbine projects and encourage others to do likewise. Its membership is around 200.

I want to visit a wind farm, where is the nearest one to me?
Most wind farms are in Cornwall, Cumbria, Wales, Yorkshire, Northern Ireland and Scotland.

What can I do to help wind energy?
One of the most helpful things you can do is to help win the debate on wind energy. Respond to letters in local and national papers, participate in radio phone-in programmes and wherever else the opportunity arises. Don't be one of the silent majority.

From 1998 you have been able to choose who supplies your electricity. 'Green' electricity is available from most electricity suppliers, in line with the new Government obligation on electricity companies to source 10% of their supply from renewable energy.

Statistics and data

How many wind farms/turbines are there in the UK?
We have a list of the operational wind farms in the UK, which will also tell you how much electricity they produce.

How much electricity does one wind turbine produce?
One 600kW wind turbine at a reasonable site would produce enough electricity to meet the annual needs of 375 households.

• The above information is from the British Wind Energy Association's web site which can be found at www.britishwindenergy.co.uk Alternatively, see their address details on page 41.

© British Wind Energy Association (BWEA)

The wind farm debate

The pros and cons of wind farms

The UK's potential resource for wind generated electricity, using wind turbines sited in windy parts of the countryside, is put at about 20% of current electricity requirements. That's about what nuclear power provides at present.

However the amount of power that can actually be obtained from the winds will depend on how many acceptable sites can be found. Currently more than thirty wind farms – groups of wind turbines on one site – have been set up, in Cornwall, Wales, Yorkshire, Scotland and elsewhere. Most have been welcomed locally, but in some locations there have been some strong local protests, chiefly over noise problems and visual intrusion.

The case for wind farms is straightforward. Wind power is clean – extracting power from the wind produces no chemical or radioactive emissions, and has minimal physical impacts on the local ecosystem. The land around the wind turbines in wind farms can be used for conventional agricultural purposes – indeed sheep seem to welcome them as windbreaks.

Birds tend to avoid moving wind turbine blades: indeed they seem much more at risk from the large national grid cables. Wind turbines are more like bird scarers. When and if needed, decommissioning is easy: when removed, wind farms leave no toxic residues or environmental damage. There are no direct fuel costs, and the cost of extracting power is bound to fall as the technology improves.

In summary, wind power is sustainable, clean and is increasingly competitive economically. Its local impacts are relatively small compared with the global impacts of using conventional fuels.

But there is also a case against wind farms.

Firstly, the local impacts are not always insignificant – local residents may be disturbed by noise and the wind farms intrude on the landscape. Some local residents have reported annoying levels of noise from the blades or the gearing systems of some wind turbines – with some, for example, finding it hard to sleep. Others have complained that the machines are ugly, and may deter tourists from the area. Some objectors feel the planning bodies have not been sufficiently rigorous in applying the necessary planning controls.

Secondly, some say that the wind programme is counterproductive – it would be better to invest in energy conservation. Some opponents feel that the wind farms produce expensive electricity and that the developers have simply taken advantage of the interim cross subsidy scheme introduced by the Government to make easy profits, paid for by consumers, whereas the amount of power generated is small compared to what could be saved if we invested instead in energy conservation measures. Finally, some say that the UK is too densely populated to be able to absorb a significant number of wind farms. Wind farms must inevitably be sited on prominent ridges and hills, and these are usually in attractive areas. These should be protected for everyone's use. If we must have wind turbines, why not put them off shore?

In summary, wind farms are noisy, ugly, expensive and are not needed or appropriate in the UK countryside.

With the foregoing in mind, it seems useful to make the following points.

> *Wind power is sustainable, clean and is increasingly competitive economically. Its local impacts are relatively small compared with the global impacts of using conventional fuels. But there is also a case against wind farms*

Firstly, the economics of wind power are improving, but profit margins are still tight. Even so the extra cost to consumers is small.

The Government's Non Fossil Fuel Obligation (NFFO) initially provided a protected market for both nuclear power and some renewables, together with a surcharge on fossil fuel generation. This fossil fuel levy was passed on ultimately to consumers, and ran at around 10% of generating costs until 1998. It raised £1.3 billion or so each year, £1.2 billion of this going to Nuclear. The small amount left over has supported just under 200 renewable projects, including 30 or so wind farms. The cost to the consumer of supporting the wind projects was very small – less than one per cent extra on their bills.

The nuclear part of the NFFO was withdrawn in 1998, and since then the cost of electricity from wind projects has continued to reduce, as the technology has improved. So the next wave of wind projects have been able to go ahead with less subsidy, and wind power is approaching commercial competitiveness.

Even so, the profit margins for bold new projects like this are tight: it is hardly a case of easy money for the developers and backers.

The NFFO system is now being replaced with a Renewables Obligation – which will require electricity suppliers to work towards obtaining 5% of their power from renewable sources by 2003 and 10% by 2010. Wind power is likely to meet a significant part of this requirement. That's not surprising since some of the latest projects are generating at prices competitive with conven-tional sources – at around 2p/kWh in some cases.

Secondly, the initial projects were generally welcomed locally – with some of the initial objectors changing their mind once the projects were up and running. This pattern of initial concern followed by general acceptance has continued.

The UK's first windfarm was at Deli farm near Delabole in Cornwall. An independent 'before and after' study indicated that 80% of the local people asked said it made no difference to their daily life, 44% approved and 40% approved strongly. In the 'before' study, 40% of local people interviewed thought it was going to be visually intrusive, but this fell to 29% after it was set up and running. Whereas many expected it to present noise problems beforehand, after it was running 80% felt this had turned out not to be a problem. The wind farm had 100,000 visitors in its first year of operation.

A subsequent Countryside Council for Wales study, in areas of Wales where wind farms have been operating, indicated that 68% of the sample felt that the wind farms had little impact and that they would be prepared to see more. Interestingly many more objections came from a control sample in an area where there were no wind farms.

And a recent study in Scotland, focusing on people living near Scotland's first four wind farms also found that the closer people lived to wind farms the more positive was their attitude to them. 67% found 'something they liked' about the Scottish wind farms, rising to 73% amongst those living closest. More-over, 74% found 'nothing they disliked' rising to 80% for those nearest. Overall it seems that people's worries prior to construction were often unfounded – for example 40% of the 430 or so respondents in the Scottish survey said they thought that there would be problems, but in the event only 9% reported any problems. Specifically, beforehand 12% though noise would be a problem, but afterward only 1% reported any disturbance.

Thirdly, the main objections have been about projects where there have been specific local problems.

The Llandinam wind farm in Wales is acceptably quiet close up, (most people are surprised at how quiet wind farms are when they first visit them) but down in the valley resonance effects seem occasionally to amplify the noise. Effects like this will have to be responded to carefully, and avoided in future. Similarly, as experience with wind farm deployment grows, siting policy can be improved to avoid interfering with sensitive local views. Full local consultation, well in advance, is an obvious priority.

Fourthly, around 70% of the 3000 or so wind turbines in Denmark are owned locally – would local ownership reduce the level of opposition in the UK? 'Your own pigs don't smell', say the Danes.

So far all the UK projects have been developed by conventional medium to large-scale companies, with some of the funding and the technology coming from overseas e.g. from Japan. Would a shift to 'co-ops', like the Danish Guilds, improve the situation in the UK, with the local community thereby benefiting directly from the project?

Fifthly, the UK has the world's best wind power resource – with Scotland having more wind power available than the rest of Europe put together.

Denmark, which is mainly flat, aims to generate 10% of its electricity from wind turbines by 2005. Surely the UK, which has a much better wind regime, can do at least as well?

Electricity generating costs

Wind energy is cheaper than both new coal-fired and nuclear power.

Technology	Plant cost (£/kW)	Fuel cost (p/kWh)	O&M* (p/kWh)	Total generating cost (p/kWh) range	average
Gas	400-600	1.1	0.3	1.8-2.2	2
Wind	700-1,000	0	0.8	1.9-3.1	2.5
Coal	750-1,000	1.1	0.6	2.6-3.25	3.1
Nuclear	1,500-2,000	0.4	0.6	5.2-8.7	6

Source: The British Wind Energy Association

If we turn our back on this option, what are the alternatives? Energy conservation is an obvious priority, but even if we can block up the leaky bucket of current very inefficient energy use system, we will still need sustainable energy supplies to fill it, i.e. we need both conservation and renewables – including offshore wind and the other renewables.

It's worth noting in this context that installing 1500 mega watts of renewable generating capacity would, according to the DTI's 1994 Energy Paper 62, avoid the emission of some 2 million tonnes of carbon p.a., at a cost of around only one per cent extra on consumers' electricity bills, via the NFFO. By comparison the Energy Saving Trust's energy conservation programme, if successful, would save around 2.5 mTCpa and add 1-2% to consumers bills – possibly more. So renewables and conservation are fairly evenly matched in terms of the cost of cutting emissions, with wind power playing a useful role in this process.

Finally, we are not faced with a static situation. As wind turbine technology develops, some of the initial problems should be resolved. For example, new, variable speed, machines are being developed which are more efficient, economic and less noisy.

The wind farm debate

The debate over wind power has become increasingly polarised in the UK, with extreme positions often being taken, particularly by the objectors, who sometimes evidently feel that wind projects are being forced on them.

One unsigned leaflet circulated in Wales in 1993 warned that Wales was 'being covered in swathes of ugly turbines to line the pockets of foreigners and greedy owners'. A little more moderately, Sir Bernard Ingham, vice president of the Country Guardian anti-wind lobby group, commented 'people who think they're attractive are aesthetically dead' (*Newsweek* 28 March,1994).

Clearly everyone is entitled to their opinion: after all, in the end it is often a subjective issue. For example, some people are very sensitive to low level noise – and

can't sleep with a fridge running. Some are very sensitive to changes in the landscape – even though of course the current UK landscape is mostly man-made, the result of centuries of modifications due to agriculture, land clearance and so on.

Some find wind farms very appealing – as witness the large number of tourists visiting them. Some local people have actually objected to not being able to see them. Some see them as ugly monstrosities, as 'lavatory brushes in the sky', while others see them as symbols of a sustainable future, and as a clear alternative to nuclear power.

Given the wide range of responses to the wind farm issue, it is understandable that the debate can become a little shrill. However, what is needed is a constructive debate on the role of renewables generally, and on exactly what the carrying capacity of a country like the UK is as far as wind turbines are concerned. Is the 20% theoretical resource too much to hope for? Will it be cut down in practice to 10% or even less? What about offshore wind? And the other renewables? What would be their impacts? For example, would short rotation arable coppicing be a better bet, more suited than wind farms to farming communities, as some suggest? Or, if carried out on a large scale, wouldn't that be to return to a 'slash and burn' approach, with its own set of environmental dangers? Aren't there likely to be just as many objections to extensive coppice plantations, wood chip incineration plants, and significantly increased local truck traffic?

Conclusion

All technologies have impacts. In general, however, the impacts of the renewables are much smaller and more local than the usually large and global impacts of conventional energy technologies. Inevitably, the land-based renewables, like wind turbines and energy crops, are likely to be the most problematic. By contrast, by the nature of their location, offshore wind for example, as well as offshore wave and tidal stream turbines, are less likely to present problems of visual intrusion – they also offer very large energy potentials. Unfortunately however, very little funding has been made available for research on wave and tidal stream technology, but a small offshore wind farm has been installed off the coast of North-umbria, and offshore wind seems likely to become a major option for the future.

However, even given a properly integrated national policy on renewable development, we would still probably have to strike a balance between these various options, and, therefore, to get to grips with land use issue.

Hopefully, however, the smaller scale and more local nature of most renewable energy technologies should make this process easier. For unlike conventional power stations, whose often large-scale, global, social and environmental costs and risks are often hidden away, the impact of renewables like wind farms is more obvious and local. Basically, the technologies are easier to understand and assess. What you see is what you get: there are no hidden costs.

Given that the nature and function of the technology is more transparent, it ought to be possible to have a constructive debate, involving a wide range of people, over how, where, on what scale and by whom renewable energy systems like wind farms should be developed.

• NATTA produces a bi-monthly journal, *Renew*, which, amongst other things, covers the wind farm debate. See page 41 for address details. Or visit NATTA's web site at technology.open.ac.uk/eeru/natta/
© *NATTA*

Bioenergy – 21st-century fuel

Information from British BioGen

Bioenergy – what is it?

Biomass is all plant and animal matter on the Earth's surface. Harvesting biomass such as crops, trees or dung and using it to generate energy, that is heat, electricity or motion, is bioenergy.

Biomass was the first fuel that mankind learned to use for energy; the first fires of primitive man burning wood for warmth and cooking. World-wide bioenergy, much of it traditional woodfuel, is still by far our most important source of non-fossil fuel energy, meeting 13% of primary energy demand. Before the First World War about 40% of the UK's agricultural land was devoted to bioenergy; fuel crop production, mainly grass and oats to feed the horses that then still drove much of the economy.

Modern bioenergy is clean, efficient and sustainable. Austria now uses bioenergy for 13% of all its energy needs and the United States generates 3% of its electricity from bioenergy. Bioenergy is the World's most important renewable energy and is quietly getting more important all the time.

Bioenergy – why do we need it?

Global energy supply is continually evolving in response to the changing needs of industry and consumers. The pace of change is accelerating as energy markets open to competition and new technologies challenge energy supply conventions. Countries are just beginning to address the overriding reality of the need to exploit more sustainable and politically secure energy resources.

The supply of fossil fuels is shifting geographically as existing sources are depleted and new, more economic resources are opened up. This change is most evident in Europe and the United States where dependence on imported energy will grow rapidly in the next decade.

The politics of environmental protection, especially with regard to climate change is forcing Governments to initiate programmes to reduce carbon emissions, improve energy efficiency and exploit less carbon intensive energy sources.

Bioenergy is at the centre of these changes as the only renewable carbon fuel with the potential to address the full range of energy markets including heat, electricity and transport.

The renewable energy strategies of both Europe and the United States expect the bioenergy sector to be pre-eminent in the global market for secure, indigenous and renewable energy supplies in the next century and to play a vital role in underpinning the overall transition to sustainable energy.

Bioenergy is the world's most important renewable energy and yet most people have never heard of it.

Fewer people still know that bioenergy provides over five times as much energy in the UK as large-scale hydroelectricity; in 1997 bioenergy accounted for 81% of all renewable energy generation in the UK.

Yet the UK has a vibrant and ambitious bioenergy industry, which includes some of the country's, and world's, largest and most well-known companies. Companies like Shell, Enron, National Power, Hydro-Agri, Yorkshire Water, Ernst and Young, Eastern Generation and BG Technology.

Bioenergy, the growing energy business, provides opportunities for all from individual householders, farmers and foresters to Local and National Government and multinational energy companies. British BioGen has 150 member organisations with expertise in all aspects of bioenergy and with real experience in real projects. To find out how you might seize the bioenergy opportunity contact British BioGen today.

• The above is an extract from *Bioenergy – 21st-century fuel*, produced by British BioGen. See page 41 for address details.

© *British BioGen*

A shining example

What is solar power and why do we need it? Paul Allen investigates.

What's the problem?

Like it or not, whenever we use energy from fossil fuels, we are dumping carbon dioxide into the atmosphere. From the beginning of the Industrial Revolution, the rate at which we burn fossil fuels has increased every year. The rise of the automobile and the easy availability of cheap petrochemicals in the 1950s and 1960s has made this increase exponential. Now, fossil fuels are used on such a vast scale that the planet is failing to cope. The build-up of carbon dioxide in the atmosphere is now recognised as a major cause of the instability in the global climate, placing vast areas of the world at risk.

The world population has doubled since 1950. By the year 2030, more than 10 billion people will inhabit the earth. There is now little doubt that we can no longer enjoy our present consumption patterns without putting at risk the future of life on earth. In the developed West, we currently enjoy the benefits of a disproportionately large share of the world's energy; yet the whole planet carries the burden of our emissions. As the global demand for electricity rises – particularly in China and the rapidly developing Eastern economies – there is little doubt that this vast increase in emissions will have dramatic consequences for the global eco-system.

The world cannot support our socio-economic activities. The time is ripe for consideration of alternative models of development.

What do we mean by being 'green'?

The roots of the modern ecological movement are diverse. Its development was an inevitable reaction against the effects of the Industrial Revolution. The energy of the Luddites, the voluntary simplicity of the Quakers, the views of nature developed by the Romantic painters and poets such as Blake and Shelley, the reaction against the rampant consumerism of the 1950s . . . , all this came to a head in the early 1970s. In 1972, Peter Harper coined the term 'alternative technology' to describe attitudes and approaches to working with nature. This idea has been with us for over twenty-five years now, an intuitive reaction to our diminishing natural environment. Although self-sufficiency was once thought to be the solution, the past two decades have seen an increased emphasis on the notion of sustainability – engaging society, rather than dropping out of it.

Meanwhile out in space

A most fascinating process is going on. Inside the sun, matter is converted directly into energy by the process of nuclear fusion, where small amounts of matter yield an enormous amount of energy. This potential is illustrated by Einstein's famous law $E = mc^2$, where E is the amount of energy created, m is the mass of matter destroyed and c is 3 x 108 metres per second – the speed of light. In fact, the sun generates a massive 3.94×10^{23} kW of power all day, every day.

This radiated energy takes about 8 minutes to cover its 93 million mile journey to reach us on earth. The total energy reaching the surface of the earth is about $80,000 \times 10^{12}$ W, or 10,000 times the current global energy demand. As it heats up the surface of the earth, it causes air to

move around the planet, creating the global windpower resource. Some of this wind energy is concentrated by the sea, giving us the world's wave power resource.

Four-fifths of the sun's energy falls on the sea, driving the water cycle. Ocean evaporation causes rain to fall on the land, creating the global hydropower resource. The remaining fifth, which falls on land, is still about 2,000 times greater than the total world energy demand. This can be captured using a variety of solar technologies.

Technologies to capture solar energy (three different kinds)

There are three different ways we can capture the sun's energy:

a) Passive solar: space heating by conscious design of buildings.

Using buildings to collect the sun's warmth was a technique the early Greek and Roman builders developed into a serious form of solar architecture, as did the builders of the Pueblo villages in the American South-West and the Inca builders in Machu Picchu. Forms of solar architecture were also developed by Muslim architects, who used the minarets of mosques as solar chimneys. The exploitation of cheap fossil fuels made solar design too troublesome to bother with until the steep rise in oil prices, orchestrated by the OPEC countries in the 1970s.

Today, passive solar design is the most commercially mature of all the solar technologies, competing very well on direct cost terms with conventional energy sources. It can provide up to 70% of a building's energy needs by using sensible design and solar orientation; the increase in cost is marginal. Large glass windows or conservatories on south-facing surfaces take advantage of large amounts of free energy. Excessive heat is avoided by using overhanging balconies or planting trees nearby – these reduce sunlight during the summer, but let it in during the winter when the sun is low and the leaves have fallen.

b) Solar thermal: using solar energy to heat water.

A solar water heater is simply water pipes painted black to improve heat absorption. The small diameter of the pipes ensures that a large surface area of water is exposed to the sun. The pipes are placed in a small 'greenhouse' to insulate them. Originally developed in response to the steep rise in oil prices in the 1970s, solar water heating got off to a very rocky start. The wild claims and poor engineering of many 'cowboy' manufacturers and installers undermined the credibility of the industry on both sides of the Atlantic.

Today, those problems are behind us. The UK alone has over 40,000 solar water heating systems. A survey in 1995 found that most were saving up to £200 per year, and around 75% of customers were 'very satisfied' with their systems. Solar water heating is commercially mature technology, competing very well with conventional energy sources – although, obviously, the payback time relates directly to the available solar resource of any particular site. Typical installation costs vary from about £800 for a 'Do It Yourself' system, to £3,000 for a commercial system which can provide approximately 60% of typical domestic hot water needs in the UK. Even though 500,000 square metres of panels are sold each year, there is room for improvement. 1.4 million households in Europe now use solar water heating, but this still only represents 1% of the potential market. The rate of installation in the UK could easily be increased with government incentives. The Dutch Ministry of Economic Affairs, for example, is working closely with industry and the energy utilities. Together, they are approaching consumers, housing corporations, property developers and municipal authorities with a campaign to ensure that some 400,000 domestic systems will be installed by 2010. Such co-operation has already put the Netherlands ahead of many of their European counterparts. The world's

largest domestic solar hot water project to date was completed at Apeldoorn, where 1,000 houses were provided with systems. The project partners learned much about the reality of cost reduction through large-scale installation and user feedback. In the UK, a project to install 100 systems will soon be completed in three developments in Swansea, Glamorgan, and Barry. It is part of a Thermie project aiming to install at least 3,000 systems in new-built properties in Germany, Denmark, the UK and the Netherlands before 1999.

c) The 'Photovoltaic effect': generating electricity from sunlight.

Exploration of the photovoltaic effect began a surprisingly long time ago. In 1839, the French scientist Bequerel noticed that when light was directed on to one side of a simple battery cell, the generated current could be increased. Thirty-four years later, the British scientist Willoughby Smith discovered that selenium was sensitive to light. He found that selenium's ability to conduct electricity increased if it was exposed to more light. This discovery inspired scientists to carry out further experiments with this rare element. In 1880, Charles Fritts developed the first selenium-based solar cell. Research continued on the selenium solar cell throughout the first half of the twentieth century, despite its very low efficiencies and expensive production costs.

The real breakthrough came in the 1950s when Bell Laboratories discovered that silicon – the second most abundant element on earth – was also sensitive to light and generated a substantial voltage when treated with certain impurities. By 1954, Bell had developed a solar cell using silicon as the base material which achieved an efficiency of 6%. The first industrial use occurred soon afterwards: the powering of a remote telephone repeater station in rural Georgia.

In the late 1950s, NASA installed a 108-cell photovoltaic array on America's first satellite, Vanguard One. The costs for such systems are understandably quite high, reaching over US$100 per watt. For earth-bound applications, where environmental and size constraints are not nearly so severe, much cheaper devices have been developed.

Although economically it is not yet a fully mature technology, photovoltaic technology is now on the threshold of a performance-to-cost capability which would permit it to make significant advances in many new market areas. With costs falling each year, photovoltaics is already commercially mature in many remote applications, where it can compete with the higher installation costs of long links to the grid or expensive generation from diesel sets. Such applications already include healthcare in the developing world, telecommunications repeaters, cathodic protection of pipelines, and marine buoys.

In grid-linked applications, photovoltaic electricity is currently almost five times more expensive than conventional electricity. This is mainly due to economic factors:

- The economies of scale support conventional technologies.
- There is still no levy on fossil and nuclear sources for polluting the environment.
- Direct subsidies to oil and gas (£9.2 million in the UK during 1996 – Greenpeace).
- Direct subsidies to coal (£6.3 million in the UK during 1996 – Greenpeace).
- Subsidies to nuclear (£11,544 million in the UK from 1990 to 1995 – Greenpeace).
- Renewables in the UK received only 2% of the subsidies directed at fossil fuels and nuclear energy in the UK from 1990 to 1995, the second lowest in the EU (Greenpeace).

During the past five years, grid-linked photovoltaic has gained cost advantages through the integration of electricity generation modules into the design of buildings. The costs of displaced building materials help offset the cost of the photovoltaic generators. Photovoltaic generators operate with no moving parts, noise or pollution, making them the most appropriate renewable energy source for use in urban areas. In the UK, there are at present only six photovoltaic roofs, in contrast to forward-thinking countries such as Germany where there are over 1,000 already in operation, with plans for many more. Such a long-term perspective builds up the skills base and technical infrastructure. Between 1976 and 1988 the cost of photovoltaic panels fell at a rate in excess of 15% per annum. As the costs approach those of conventional building cladding or roofing materials, solar power will allow buildings to generate their own electricity – selling it to the national grid when they have a surplus, and buying electricity back when they have a deficit.

To provide a PV power supply

SOLAR

capable of meeting the demand from a typical domestic energy-efficient house costs in the region of £20,000. Although this may seem quite high, it is not an unreasonable proportion of the cost of building a house.

The next move – to maturity and beyond

If we are to see the necessary commercial maturity required to implement solar thermal and solar electric systems on the scale required to have a significant effect on global warming, we will need to see a more co-ordinated incubation process. In the Netherlands, for instance, the Government, power companies, architects, planners, financial institutions, local authorities, scientists and manufacturers are co-operating in order to develop solar energy. Projects such as the Nieuw Sloten estate in Amsterdam show what can be achieved. By integrating PV modules into 34 low-level and 37 high-rise properties, the project generates 250kW peak into the local grid, enough for 100 households. Needless to say, all the houses have been sold!

As electricity markets are opened up in 1998, new economic systems must be put in place. Plans are already under way for green electricity companies. This will make renewable energy available to all consumers for only a small increase in cost and offer a fair price to renewable energy generators. At first this offer may concentrate on large industrial users, but domestic consumers must also be given this choice through a 'green tariff' system. The Dutch energy company Nuon is currently using such a system to fund a sixfold increase in its solar electric generating capacity between 1996 and the year 2000, bringing it up to 6,000 megawatt hours per annum. The system has proved both cost effective and popular – so much so

that the district council in Apeldoorn has recently switched to the green tariff for its public buildings.

What's the solution?

Clearly, if solar energy is to make a significant contribution towards social, economic, and ecological sustainability, we will need to see a combination of the following factors:

- Pioneering solar projects such as CAT's solar roof, which illustrate what is possible and help kick-start the economies of scale.
- New economic systems such as the green tariff, making green electricity accessible to everyone regardless of where they live, and offering a fair price to solar generators.
- A large-scale, centrally-funded energy-efficiency programme to help us all do more with less.
- Diversion of all subsidies away from fossil fuels into subsidies for renewables.
- A new era of co-operation between industry, local and national government, architects, planners, power companies and customers, to bring about the solar revolution.

In its election agenda, the new Labour administration made many claims regarding its support for renewable energy. Now is the time to demonstrate the Government's genuine commitment. Let's follow the shining solar examples set by the Netherlands, Germany, and our other European partners. Action is urgently needed from the developed economies to produce a mature programme for the advancement of solar and other renewable technologies. This is vital if we are to help China and the emerging Eastern economies 'leapfrog' excessive fossil fuel emissions and move directly to the sustainable alternatives. We must act now, before the global cost in terms of climate change becomes too high for all of us.

Solar electric power

Information from Greenpeace

Solar electric (photovoltaic or 'PV') panels produce electricity directly from sunlight, the Earth's primary source of energy. Despite its notoriously rainy climate the UK would get 2/3 of its electricity from solar if all suitably oriented roofs were equipped with solar panels.[1] Even on overcast days there is enough diffuse daylight for solar electric panels to generate some electricity. If all of the sunlight hitting the UK in one average day was harnessed and converted into electrical power, it would be enough to fulfil the whole of the UK's electricity needs for 2 whole years.[2]

Solar power is a vital technology to replace fossil fuels, the major cause of climate change. A one kilowatt array of solar electric panels covering 10 square metres will save the emission of nearly one tonne of carbon dioxide emissions every year.[3] Of all the forms of renewable energy, solar electric is the only one that most homeowners can produce themselves. Houses fitted with solar electric panels can export their surplus solar electricity to the grid and become miniature power stations generating pollution-free electricity in our towns and cities. The handful of buildings in the UK currently using solar electricity could, with Government and industry support, become millions.

However, up until now, householders who wished to take environmentally responsible action and install solar electric panels have felt ripped off. Typically, a solar householder has been charged 6-7p per unit of electricity imported whilst being offered only 2.5-4p for each unit of electricity they export. This seems particularly unfair when they are producing clean electricity and the vast majority of what they import is generated by burning fossil fuels, with concomitant emissions of CO_2 which damage the climate. This is a perverse disincentive when Government is striving to achieve its climate change strategy and has, quite rightly, set itself a target to get 10% of UK electricity from renewable energy by 2010.

This solar scandal has now been broken thanks to a deal brokered by Greenpeace with power company TXU-Europe (Eastern Energy). For the first time in the UK, householders with solar panels will now be offered 'net metering' under the brand name SolarNet. This means that their exported solar electricity will get the same price per unit (kWh) as the electricity they import from the grid. This net metering contract will be available to solar electric householders wherever they are in the UK.

Net metering is particularly important to domestic solar electric users because their solar electricity output peaks during daytime whilst their home is likely to be using comparatively little electricity. So it is important to be able to use the grid like a battery, exporting to the grid during daytime in order that the solar electricity is not wasted, and taking electricity off the grid when it is dark. On the other hand, many businesses tend to use most electricity during office hours, so the electricity exported by solar homes usefully coincides with their electricity requirements.

Because of the disincentives in the UK against domestic photovoltaic panels there are only about ten grid-connected solar electric houses in the UK. This net metering deal offered by TXU is a very significant step towards achieving a dramatic increase in solar electric homes.

Although net metering is new to the UK it is already happening in other countries. In the USA, net metering applies in many States including California. The USA produced 1/3 of the world's photovoltaic panels last year.

As well as its environmental benefits, solar power is an opportunity for the UK to capture a share of the jobs and money in the expanding global photovoltaic (PV) industry, which grew 32% last year. A strong drive for PV in the UK would reap large commercial rewards. In Japan, where the Government has set a target of 70,000 grid-connected solar roofs by 2010, PV production increased 63% in 1999 to meet the demand.[4] The top producers are Kyocera, Sharp, Sanyo, with Canon also in the list, a roll-call of firms that have become UK household names with high-tech products and who see big market potential for PV.

The story in the UK is in stark contrast. Although the world's biggest solar PV company is British – BP Solarex – it does not manufacture PV in the UK, and recently moved the HQ of its solar business to the USA. This is an indictment of UK industrial policy which has failed to set a constructive framework for the PV industry in the UK and has no solar electric targets similar to those of Japan, USA or Germany.

There are strong environmental and business reasons that solar electricity should not only qualify for net metering, but should command a premium price. For example, the German Government agreed a new 'feed-in' law in February that sets a price of 99pfg ($0.50) per unit (kWh) for solar electricity.

References
1. *The Potential Generating Capacity of PV Clad Buildings in the UK*, ETSU 1992.
2. Data from *Building Homes with Solar Power, A Greenpeace report based on original research by HGa Consulting Engineers*, Greenpeace, 1996, 32pp.
3. *A Realisable Renewable Energy Future*, John A. Turner, *Science*, 1999, v.285, p.687. Also data in ref. II above.
4. Figures from *Photovoltaic News*, Feb 2000, v.19, no.2

BP bows to solar power pressure

Rethink after shareholder rebellion. By Terry Macalister.

BP Amoco is considering a massive expansion of its renewable energy programme over and above the $250m it has already earmarked to spend over the next five years.

In a move that will delight its environmental critics, such as Greenpeace, the oil major plans to approach leading investors to see whether they would support a significant change of tack.

The move follows a rebellion at the recent annual meeting when a surprising number of shareholders voted in favour of a 'green' motion despite opposition from the board.

Any increase in investment would almost certainly be centred on solar power in which BP Amoco has already established an industry lead. A senior executive privately admitted both the company and its main investors had been shaken by the vote at the annual meeting.

But the BP Amoco executive said the group was determined to act positively on the issue. 'At the next round of meetings with investors if they do not raise the issue, which I am sure they will, then we will. If they want us to step out a bit then let's hear them give us their support,' he explained.

The investment would represent a sea change in thinking about the future of the group, which is already moving away from oil to more environmentally-friendly fuels such as gas. But the BP Amoco executive said there was no question of the second biggest oil company in the world becoming a renewable energy group overnight. It might take 20 or 30 years before that happened.

The potential commitment to renewable energy came on a day when a leading figure in the sector predicted solar power would become a multi-billion dollar market. Dr Jeremy Leggett, chief executive of the Solar Century, told an alternative

energy conference called by Dresdner Kleinwort Benson that solar power would 'be to the 21st century what the microchip was to the 20th'. He said the fossil fuel sector was entering its autumn years.

Plans to spend $250m over five years are significant but a drop in the ocean when put next to the group's other investment plans. Yesterday it said it intended to spend $10bn to $11bn, mainly on gas projects, over the next two years.

Gas production is set to jump 8bn cubic ft a day by the end of this year, giving BP Amoco the equivalent of 3.6m barrels of liquids, two-thirds of the group's production portfolio. Oil output will remain steady at 2m barrels per day.

BP Amoco, which has just won approval for the takeover of America's Arco, unveiled record first-quarter profits of $2.7bn. These were up 256% on the same period last year, mainly boosted by a big turnround in crude prices.

BP Amoco chief executive Sir John Browne said the outlook for the year was good with a 'broadly positive environment'. The company would now be entering a period of consolidation however with divestments and cost savings to come. BP Amoco shares fell 19.5p to end the day at 577.5p.

Energy – the changing climate

Royal Commission calls for transformation in the UK's use of energy to counter climate change

As a contribution to global efforts to prevent climate change running out of control, the United Kingdom should plan for a reduction of 60% over the next 50 years in the amounts of carbon dioxide it produces by burning fossil fuels. This is one of the key conclusions of a major report published today by the Royal Commission on Environmental Pollution. The report – *Energy – the Changing Climate* – explores what that will mean for industry and ordinary households, and how government policies need to change.

Speaking at Westminster this morning, the Chairman of the Royal Commission, Sir Tom Blundell, said: 'Recklessly causing large-scale disruptions to climate by burning fossil fuels will affect all countries. It is the poorest that would suffer most. We cannot expect other nations to do their part in countering this threat – least of all if they are much less wealthy – unless we demonstrate we are really serious about it.'

The UK has already played a leading role in international negotiations, and the Royal Commission thinks it can, and should, continue to do so. The amounts of carbon dioxide the UK emits are now significantly lower than in 1990, but much of the progress so far has been fortuitous. The Commission welcomes the government's goal of a 20% reduction from the 1990 level by 2010 as a major step in the right direction. It recommends that this should become a firm target, but expresses doubts whether the measures at present proposed will achieve it. The UK lags far behind many other European countries in developing the renewable energy technologies that will become much more important in future, and in the very inefficient ways heat is supplied to homes.

The primary purpose of the report is to look much further ahead

than the UK's draft Climate Change Programme. The Commission highlights the difficulties there will be in maintaining a 20% reduction beyond 2010, let alone making much larger reductions. It emphasises the need to start now on making reduction of carbon dioxide emissions a key factor in the planning and design of power stations and buildings of all types, many of which will still be in use in 2050. Ways have to be found of achieving sustainable solutions within liberalised energy markets, in which the emphasis has so far been on minimising price per unit in order to maximise sales of energy.

At the moment, use of energy, predominantly in the form of oil, gas or coal, is continuing to increase, both worldwide and in the UK. The Royal Commission has investigated:

- the scope over the next 50 years for replacing fossil fuels by expanding the UK's use of renewable energy sources, such as wind power, solar energy and energy crops. Their use will have to expand to well beyond the 10% of electricity generation which the government has suggested as a target for 2010
- whether nuclear power could be part of the solution. Nuclear waste

will first have to be dealt with to the satisfaction of the scientific community and the general public. People are unlikely to accept new nuclear power stations unless they are part of a strategy that also delivers radical improvements in energy efficiency and an equal opportunity for deploying renewable energy sources that can compete in terms of costs and reduced environmental impacts

- the potential for reducing the large losses within the energy system, especially the large amounts of heat wasted at power stations
- the potential for industry, households and motorists to make much more efficient use of energy
- the possibility that some of the carbon dioxide produced when fossil fuels are burnt could be recovered and piped safely away into geological formations under the seabed.

To show the scale of the changes required to achieve a 60% reduction in UK carbon dioxide emissions, the Royal Commission describes four scenarios for 2050 representing various combinations of these approaches. It emphasises that these scenarios are illustrative. But all of them involve a reversal of the previous trend of growing energy use, and in three of them the total amount of energy used would have to be much less than today.

Some of the scenarios might involve significant changes in lifestyles. All involve constructing many new energy installations, with resulting impacts on the environment. The challenge climate change poses for the world is so fundamental however that a complete transformation in the UK's use of energy will be an essential part of an effective global response.

The Royal Commission's report makes 87 recommendations. Many of them are addressed to the devolved administrations in Scotland, Wales and Northern Ireland as well as to the government at Westminster. Among the 19 key recommendations are:

- a long-term programme to cut considerably the energy used in buildings of all types
- creation of a Sustainable Energy Agency to boost energy efficiency in all sectors and link that to the rapid development of renewable energy sources

- a tax on fuels that give rise to carbon dioxide emissions (preferably Europe-wide), replacing the government's planned energy tax on industry and business
- using the resulting revenue to reduce fuel poverty, as well as boost new and more sustainable technologies
- a fundamental review of the financing, management and regulation of electricity networks (like the national grid), in order to encourage renewable energy sources and combined heat and power plants, serving whole neighbourhoods or even individual houses
- quadrupling government support for energy-related research and development to bring it in line with the present EU average. Government expenditure on R & D fell by more than 80% between 1987 and 1998, and private sector spending appears to have fallen too.

Sir Tom Blundell said: 'Energy policies must command public assent and be compatible with an improving quality of life. If UK industry is to remain competitive, it has to shape

up to the very different world that lies ahead. We also have to overcome the particular UK problem that, because of inadequate insulation, several million people cannot afford to keep their homes comfortably warm in winter.'

He added: 'The problems are complex and there are no easy answers. We hope the analysis and recommendations in our report will begin the wide debate that will be essential if the UK and the whole world community are to rise successfully to the radical challenge that climate change is now posing.'

- *Energy – the Changing Climate* is available from the Stationery Office (Cm 4749, price £27.00), or the full text of the report can be downloaded free of charge from the Commission's website (www.rcep.org.uk). Because the Commission believes the issues raised are of concern to everybody, it has produced a free summary of the report, and is sending this to every secondary school, public library, university and college in the United Kingdom. This summary is also available on the Commission's website at www.rcep.org.uk

© Royal Commission on Environmental Pollution

Energy targets would change face of Britain

By James Meikle

A British landscape and coastline dominated by wind farms, with turbines on and under the sea and on much of the land, was yesterday sketched out by scientists who recommended a 60% cut in carbon dioxide emissions over the next 50 years.

There would be hardly a stretch of coastline from which a huge green power plant would not be seen as tides, wind, waves and sunshine filled an energy gap left by the shrinking use of conventional fuels such as coal, oil and gas. Swaths of agricultural land would also be turned over to energy crops, such as fast-growing willow, for a new generation of local green power stations.

Prices for electricity and other energy sources would also have to rise steadily – helped by a new carbon tax – to reduce demand, said the Royal Commission on Environmental Pollution. It challenged political parties to go much further in helping Britain to give a lead in measures to slow climate change.

Britons would have to change their energy-guzzling lifestyles to make a major dent in soaring carbon dioxide levels, with the money raised from extra taxes being used to provide better insulation in poor people's homes. Businesses might also need

subsidies to compete at international level if other countries did not introduce similar taxes, said the commission.

Its report, *Energy – the Changing Climate*, said that the government's current target for reducing 1990s carbon dioxide levels by 20% by 2010 was welcome but did not go nearly far enough. The commission wanted cuts of 60% by 2050 and 80% by 2100.

Although the amounts of carbon dioxide Britain sends into the atmosphere are significantly lower than 10 years ago, that is largely because gas has replaced coal in power stations. Making further significant inroads will be difficult as car congestion increases.

The commission offered four ways in which its targets could be reached. 'All involve substantial changes and impacts. There is no free lunch,' it said.

Its chairman, Sir Tom Blundell, said that Britain should 'embark now on a pathway that leads to a sustainable energy policy that protects the interests of our children and grandchildren and the generations after them'.

But, he said, 'changing our production and consumption of energy to protect the environment and climate must also seek to achieve social justice and reduce fuel poverty, to increase the quality of life, and to protect or enhance the competitiveness of industry'.

He added: 'Recklessly causing large-scale disruption to climate by burning fossil fuels will affect all countries. It is the poorest that would suffer most. We cannot expect other nations to do their part in countering this threat – least of all if they are much less wealthy – unless we demonstrate we are really serious about it.'

The commission recognised the value of nuclear power in providing carbon-free energy but did not believe it was indispensable. Most existing plants would have ceased operation by 2020 and no new ones should be built until the problem of managing nuclear waste had been solved to the satisfaction of scientists and the public.

There was an option of using fossil fuel plants, capturing the carbon dioxide and storing it underground. Big new plants would be necessary to fill the gaps when the weather prevented full use of wind and sea turbines or solar power.

The report also said that wind farms must not damage landscapes or wildlife.

Michael Meacher, the environment minister, said the commission was 'right to highlight how enormous the challenge of climate change really is. We must rise to this, but cannot do it alone.'

But Stephen Tindale, chief policy adviser for Greenpeace, said: 'This report confirms that fossil fuel economies such as the UK's are on the wrong path, but it also shows that wind and solar power can break

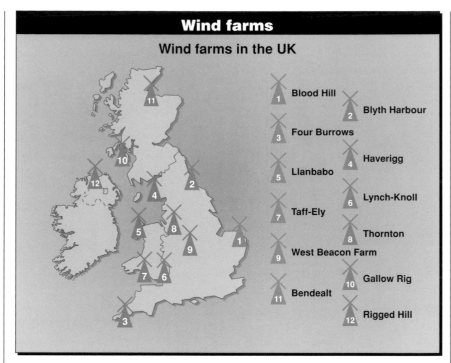

Wind farms

Wind farms in the UK

1 Blood Hill
2 Blyth Harbour
3 Four Burrows
4 Haverigg
5 Llanbabo
6 Lynch-Knoll
7 Taff-Ely
8 Thornton
9 West Beacon Farm
10 Gallow Rig
11 Bendealt
12 Rigged Hill

our addiction to oil, coal and gas. It makes clear that tinkering around the edges, which is all governments are doing now, won't stop climate change wrecking lives and economies in places like Mozambique, or prevent sea level rise flooding large parts of the UK.'

2050: The future of power

Scenario 1
60% cut in carbon dioxide; no rise in energy demand
• Two hundred wind farms 1km out to sea, 10,000 small wave-power turbines under sea, thousands more in rivers. Barrage across the Severn. Solar panels on most roofs. Wind farms on 1% of land.
• Either 46 nuclear power stations the size of Sizewell-B or 46 fossil fuel power stations with equipment for trapping and storing carbon dioxide, 15% of farmland growing crops for thousands of small local 'green' power plants. Gradual rise in energy prices, improved insulation in old housing.
• More traffic and aircraft with more efficient engines. Cars powered by fuel cells with hydrogen from oil and gas

Scenario 2
60% cut in carbon dioxide; 36% cut in energy demand
• Two hundred wind farms at sea, 10,000 small wave-power turbines under sea, thousands more in rivers and streams. Barrage across Severn estuary.

• Wide use of solar panels, but only half of scenario one, wind farms on 0.5% of land, no nuclear power, 15% of farmland growing crops for thousands of green power plants.
• Big rise in energy prices. Cars powered by fuel cells. More energy-efficient housing

Scenario 3
60% cut in carbon dioxide; 36% cut in energy use
• Two hundred windfarms at sea, 10,000 small wave-power turbines under sea, thousands more in rivers and streams. No Severn barrage. Little use of solar panels
• Either 19 new Sizewell-B power stations or similar number fossil fuel plants with carbon dioxide put underground. Few wind farms on land, 2% of farms growing crops for 1,000 green power plants. Big rise in energy prices. Traffic and aircraft use falling, cars use fuel cells, energy-efficient housing

Scenario 4
60% cut in carbon dioxide; 47% cut in energy demand
• Windpower offshore and on land only half levels of scenario one, use of crops for fuel same as scenario three, relatively little use of solar panels. Barrage across the Severn
• Wavepower and tidal streams same as other scenarios, no new power stations

© Guardian Newspapers Limited 2000

Positive futures

A look at the future of energy and renewable energy sponsored by unit[e] in association with the Guardian

Your energy

The choices we make as consumers today affect the lifestyles we lead tomorrow. As consumers, we all have a role in influencing the market, because consumer choice is what drives the market. The market in electricity, for example.

We are all consumers of electricity. We use it in most of the things we do, whether it's lighting our homes, listening to music, washing our clothes, refrigerating our food or running our computers. There is no doubt that electricity is an essential part of our lives. We have little choice when it comes to consuming electrical energy.

But we do have a a choice when it comes to purchasing electrical energy. Since the deregulation of the energy industry, and the recent introduction of competition into the domestic energy market, consumers are able to choose their electricity supplier.

Your choice

Traditionally, electricity has been generated by the burning of fossil fuels – oil, gas and coal. Latterly, the nuclear energy industry has become a major source of electricity. Now, due to technological advances in the industry, that choice is made broader. We can also produce our electricity from renewable sources. Renewable energy is produced from harnessing the power from wind or water or the sun's rays. Using these sources of energy does not deplete the earth's resources, nor pollute the environment. Renewable energy is the energy of the future. But you may be pleased to hear that you can choose to be supplied with this energy right now. Faced with the choice, wouldn't you buy your electricity generated from renewable sources? Well, now you do have the choice. It's your call.

The energy of the future – today

Renewable energy is clean, sustainable, realistic and affordable. And it's available today – we need only tap into it

The world's fastest-growing energy industries are now renewables like wind and solar power. Some of the world's largest companies like Shell and BP believe that half the world's power will come from them within 50 years and are now investing many billions of pounds in their development.

Meanwhile, we face an energy crisis not of provision but of pollution and waste. To prevent global warming which may define the next century just as war and technological advances have the last 100 years, we must reduce our dependence on polluting fossil fuels. All governments and most people recognise this. The science and the arguments are clear. Only the time scale is in doubt.

Apart from the unknown effects of global warming, the profligate use of polluting energy like coal and oil costs Britain billions of pounds every year in poor health, acid rain, damage to buildings, destruction of the environment and clearing up contamination and oil spills. Renewable energy offers a realistic social, economic and environmental alternative, as well as jobs and exports. The benefits are undoubted: wind, solar and wave energy are abundant and can be tapped once the tech-

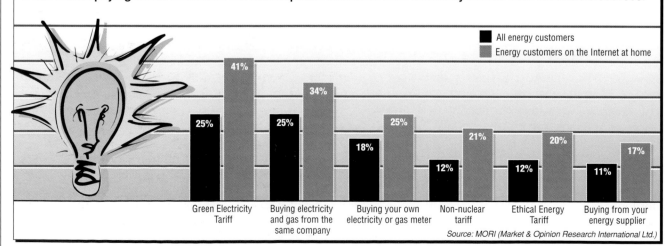

Future domestic energy

One in four energy consumers is interested in 'green' electricity. A new MORI study shows that 25% of domestic electricity customers, representing 5.7 million households, would be interested in a 'green' electricity tariff, even if this means paying a little more than the lowest prices to ensure their electricity comes from renewable sources.

Legend:
- All energy customers
- Energy customers on the Internet at home

Category	All energy customers	Energy customers on the Internet at home
Green Electricity Tariff	25%	41%
Buying electricity and gas from the same company	25%	34%
Buying your own electricity or gas meter	18%	25%
Non-nuclear tariff	12%	21%
Ethical Energy Tariff	12%	20%
Buying from your energy supplier	11%	17%

Source: MORI (Market & Opinion Research International Ltd.)

nology has been developed and mastered. Other renewable technologies, like landfill gas, derive from society's waste. The potential for their development and their advantages are almost limitless and universal.

Most countries are still paying heavily for the industrial revolution. Today, with resources scarcer, populations growing and the real costs of pollution and outdated industrial practices well known, there is an inevitable, if slow move toward the next revolution. It is being built on environmental efficiency and new technologies that have leapt ahead in the past 20 years and are now set to change the way we live by allowing us to harness and efficiently convert the natural power of the air, the sun or the seas to electricity.

Renewable energy is clean, sustainable, realistic and affordable. And it's available today – we need only tap into it

The change is being held up by political will, corporate and governmental inertia, and vested interests who would prefer to keep the status quo. Unhappily, the cards are still stacked against renewables getting a real foothold. Old power sources like nuclear, coal and oil have been protected and subsidised. Energy prices do not reflect the costs to society of waste and inefficiency.

But for the first time liberalisation of energy markets is beginning to let us choose the power we use. Choosing renewable energy is a small start to a more sustainable society that the consumer can make, and a big way of persuading governments and companies to address widespread concerns.

- Contributors: John Vidal, *Guardian* environment editor; Paul Brown, *Guardian* environment correspondent; Crispin Aubrey, editor of *Wind Directions* magazine; Jonathan Theobald, environment journalist; Nick Gallie, managing director of Navajo2 PR.

© *Guardian Newspapers Limited 2000*

25 ways to save the planet!

See how you rate in this simple evaluation of how green your lifestyle is!

Thousands of years ago our ancestors lived without making much of an impact on the natural resources of the planet. As the centuries passed we have made more and more of an impact and now we are burning up our natural resources and polluting the planet like there was no tomorrow. Given that our descendants will not think much of us if there is no tomorrow worth living in, what can we do about it?

The secrets are to achieve more with less and to work with the natural processes that kept the world going for those millions of years before the advent of 'Progress'.

Some of the following suggestions are easier than others; some are OK for country dwellers but impossible for high-rise tenants and, para-doxically, some are easier for those on low incomes.

So, here are 25 suggestions from which you can pick and mix. Remember, they may apply equally to home, place of education or workplace. And have fun doing them – if it's a chore, you won't keep it up for long. Why not check them and see how many you do already? Find out how you rate.

Energy and building

- Turn it off. Don't leave lights or appliances on when unnecessary – including those with LCDs (like video recorders) and stand-bys.
- Keep it in. Invest in draught-proofing, insulation and low-energy light bulbs, which will all pay for themselves quite quickly. Consider installing a porch, conservatory (unheated) and double glazing which will save energy and have other benefits, but have a long financial payback.
- Turn it down. Heating: make sure your equipment is efficient and well controlled and, if it doesn't harm your health, turn it down a couple of notches. Gas is better than coal and electricity, which you should avoid. If installing a new gas central heating boiler, fit a condensing or 'on demand' model – much more efficient (but not compatible with solar water heating).
- Hot pipes and tanks should be very well lagged to cut down heat loss.
- Use environmentally sound building materials. For building or DIY jobs, always use the most environmentally sound materials – low energy to produce, local if possible and non-polluting.
- Get an energy audit. Before buying a house, get an energy audit done – it could save you £1000s.
- Consider whether a solar water heating system will work in your house – it will cost £900-£1300 through a Solar Club and will provide up to 60% of your hot water.
- Buy 'Green' electricity.

Getting there

- Minimise use of the private car. Cycle, walk, use public transport, cut out unnecessary journeys and share cars. If you can, live nearer your work or school or work from home. When necessary use a taxi.
- If you do sometimes need a car then join (or start) a car pool.
- Avoid going by plane. It is by far the most polluting means of travel.

Shopping

- Avoid goods with unnecessary packaging.

- Avoid food and drink imported from distant countries (apart from fair-traded goods) and support more local produce – think of the energy used to transport it here.
- Choose the most environmentally friendly products – especially detergents and bleaches – but be careful about inaccurate claims by manufacturers.
- Remember the four Rs – reduce, reuse, repair and recycle. They are more beneficial in that order – it's better to find another use for something, repair it or recycle but better still don't buy it in the first place if it's not needed.
- Buy low-energy appliances. There are now labelling systems to guide you. Get the smallest fridge to meet your needs.
- If you have money to invest choose an ethical scheme – comparable benefits and a more positive use for your assets.
- Find ways of enjoying yourself that involve less travel and buying fewer things, such as sport.

Food, growing and health
- Eat more fresh vegetables and fruit, locally grown and organic if possible. Cut down on processed and frozen food. Eat a low-meat or vegetarian diet (it uses less land). Get more of your protein from cereal, grains, beans, nuts and dairy produce.
- Reduce your water use.
- If you can, compost your kitchen refuse and any paper and cardboard which is not suitable for recycling. If you can't do it yourself then give it to someone else who has a garden or allotment or encourage your council to run a composting scheme.
- Take care of yourself – with a good diet and exercise.

Action
- Consider getting involved in something to improve your local community. There are all sorts of groups active in doing this. Help to create and keep wild and natural areas safe from urban development.
- Engage in the democratic process via your local council and political parties. Consider joining a pressure group, local or national – like Friends of the Earth, a transport group, Earth First, Greenpeace, WWF, Oxfam, World Development Movement or our own Alternative Technology Association.
- Keep your mind open and enquiring. There are changes in technology, new ideas and new information all the time. Always keep asking what effect our actions are having on the lives of the rest of the population of the planet.

• The above information is from the Centre for Alternative Technology's web site which can be found at www.cat.org.uk

Act now

Information from WWF International

If you're concerned about global warming, you're not alone. This is where you can come for ideas about turning down the heat in your daily life.

Using less energy means less carbon pollution. For instance, if your electricity comes from a coal-fired power station, every unit of power you save means around three less units of energy that have to be burned as fuel! That's a direct cut in carbon pollution.

And using clean, renewable energy like solar power or wind power means no carbon pollution at all.

WWF's message is that solving global warming isn't about doing without. Today's energy-efficient technologies can deliver the same or a better level of service with less impact on the environment. The only real difference you might notice is lower power bills.

Here are a few tips on what you can do and how you can use your

spending power to combat global warming.

Be an efficient consumer
- Buy the most energy-efficient household appliances you can afford. In Europe, look for 'A' class products. Refrigerators in particular are large domestic electricity users that operate throughout the day. An energy-wasting refrigerator will be burning a hole in your pocket for 10 to 15 years. But if you buy an energy-efficient model you'll more than earn back any extra costs through savings on energy bills over the lifetime of the product.
- Replace normal lightbulbs with energy-efficient compact fluorescent lamps. They use around one-quarter of the energy to deliver the same light. Start with lamps that you use most – you'll save the most money and prevent the most CO_2 emission.
- Turn off equipment like TVs, stereos and printers when you're not using them. That little red light means they're still using power even when not switched on. If you're buying a new model, look for a type that uses little or no power in 'stand-by' mode.

Getting around
- Avoid using your car for local shopping or short journeys.
- If you buy a new car, ask about a model with a hybrid engine. This uses the engine to drive an on-board electric motor. The performance is similar but fuel consumption is roughly half of a

conventional car. Or look for models with gasoline direct injection engines. Their fuel consumption is around 20 per cent less than average.

- If you want to avoid being a climate destroyer, don't buy a sport utility vehicle. If you live in the United States, why not help WWF in making sure SUVs are cleaner and at least conform to the same fuel consumption standards as normal cars?

Energy-saving at home

- Check out web sites that allow you to do your own home energy audit. Type 'home+energy+audit' into search engines and let them do the research for you. If you live in the United States, try ENERGYguide.com for unbiased advice.
- Don't use electric heating – it's extremely energy wasteful.

Buy clean energy

- Ask your energy company whether you can buy 'green electricity'. Increasing numbers of utilities are selling renewable energy. It doesn't mean you have a windmill in your garden: the utility guarantees that the 'green electricity' you buy will be generated elsewhere from renewable energy sources and fed into the grid. It helps the renewable energy industry develop more rapidly and push out more polluting forms of energy.
- Look into buying solar photovoltaic (PV) panels for the roof of your house to generate some clean power of your own.

Your investments

- If you have investments, wouldn't it be a good idea to make sure your hard-earned money is benefiting companies that are manufacturing and trading in the solutions to global warming, or at least in sectors that don't contribute to the problem? Ask your financial adviser about the pros and cons and how best to arrange this.

  WWF can't offer individual investment advice but in general try and steer clear of oil companies, the

---

WWF's message is that solving global warming isn't about doing without

---

coal industry and car companies – they are among the main groups which have contributed millions of dollars to lobby against action that would limit carbon pollution.

Spread the word

- Tell your family, friends and colleagues about global warming. Get involved in starting a programme where you work or study to save energy, use renewable energy and cut global warming pollution.
- Suggest your company arranges an energy audit of its premises and production processes. Buildings are big energy users, so are industrial electric motors. Technology is developing all the time and what was energy-efficient 10 years ago is now probably obsolete. A commercial energy auditing company will probably conduct an audit free of charge and recoup its fee by sharing in

---

the cost-saving that your company realises by following the auditors' recommendations.

Political action

- Ask your political representatives to do more to reduce CO_2 emissions in your neighbourhood, city and country.
- If you're active in politics, or just interested in inspiring examples of what cities are doing around the world to reduce carbon dioxide emissions, check out the International Council for Local Environmental Initiatives (ICLEI). It's the antidote to the snail's pace of the international climate negotiations. Is where you live one of the 300 municipalities involved in ICLEI's Cities for Climate Protection campaign?

More solutions information

- Find out more about global warming solutions by searching the web for technologies such as 'solar power', 'wind power', 'fuel cells' and 'hybrid engines'.

• The above information is an extract from WWF International's web site which can be found at www.panda.org

© WWF International

– WE'RE SENDING THE ENERGY COMPANIES A MESSAGE – AND GREEN ENERGY!

Money for nothing

We spend billions every year heating our homes and running electrical appliances. That bill could easily be slashed. Helen Jones explains how.

Do you know how much your quarterly electricity bill is? A third of consumers don't have a clue. 'It's astounding. We spend more than £4bn a year running the lights and appliances in our homes, but many people don't know what it costs them or the savings they can make,' says Eoin Lees, chief executive of the Energy Savings Trust (EST), which has carried out a survey of consumer attitudes towards energy consumption.

The EST discovered that although 79% of people claim to have an 'environmental conscience', only 8% consider energy efficiency a key factor when buying household appliances.

'Much of the electricity used in the UK's homes is needlessly wasted and the resultant carbon dioxide released may contribute to global warming,' says Lees. 'Clearly people see the environment as important, but they haven't made the link between switching on an appliance, the energy it uses and the carbon dioxide that it sends into the atmosphere.'

The government wants to reduce carbon dioxide emissions by 20% in the next 10 years and is working with the EST to persuade consumers to cut energy consumption.

But if you are apathetic about the environmental message, then the savings you can make may encourage you to take action. A few simple steps can save you up to £250 a year and as the nights draw in, make your home a warmer and cosier place.

Household appliances

We consume £1.2bn worth of electricity every year just running fridges and freezers. Every time you open the door it takes the appliance three minutes to regain its temperature. One way of saving money is to ensure that your fridge/freezer is regularly defrosted and that food is

allowed to cool before storing. Don't put your fridge next to a cooker or boiler, washing machine or dishwasher if you can avoid it, because it will use more energy to keep cool. If your fridge/freezer is more than 10 years old then it is probably worth getting a new one. A new appliance can save you up to £45 a year. All new appliances have to carry an EU energy label which gives details of energy efficiency. Those rated 'A' are the most energy efficient and as a result are often more expensive than those lower down the scale.

As well as the EU energy label, look out for the EST's 'energy efficiency recommended' label. Products which exceed criteria laid down by the trust and an independent panel of experts will be entitled to carry the label.

Washing machines, tumble dryers and dishwashers also use substantial amounts of electricity – again it's worth investing in a new more efficient model if yours is more than 10 years old. For maximum savings always wait until you have a full load before running the appliance

and use a lower temperature – a 40C wash cycle uses 30% less electricity than a 60C cycle and many detergents work just as well at lower temperatures.

Always switch your TV standby off. Every year TVs use £50m-worth of electricity just waiting to be fully switched on.

Lighting

Energy-efficient lightbulbs, although more expensive than conventional ones, save money in the long run as they use only 25% of the electricity of a normal lightbulb and last up to 10 times longer. If every home in Britain installed just three of them, it would save enough energy to power all the UK's street lights.

Heating

Replacing an old boiler could save 20% on your fuel bills and if it's a condensing boiler with full heating controls, you could save up to 45%. Condensing boilers are the most efficient because they typically convert around 88% of the fuel into heat compared with 72% for standard boilers. New boilers, like other appliances, carry an EU efficiency rating from A to G. A central heating system with full heating controls could save you up to £85 a year.

Insulation

Walls lose more heat than any other part of your home. If you live in a home built after the 1930s then it is likely to have cavity walls which can be insulated. It's a straightforward process and can reduce heat loss by up to 60% and save £75 to £150 on your fuel bills each year. Older houses are likely to need solid wall insulation. This is more expensive and involves insulating and then weatherproofing external walls.

You may already have loft insulation but if it's not thick enough then you will still lose a lot of heat. Insulation that is at least 20cm thick can save up to 20% on your heating costs.

Double glazing is also an option, particularly if you have to replace old windows. Double Low E glazing costs about £250 2more than normal double glazing but it will cut £30 to £40 from your bills each year.

New homes

If you are considering buying a new home, then some of the hard work will be done for you. From January 1, 2001 house builders will have to provide prospective buyers with information on the energy efficiency levels of all new homes. Construction minister Nick Raynsford says: 'This new requirement will give prospective buyers and first occupiers an idea of how energy efficient the home is and help to promote energy efficiency as a factor in people's decisions on which home to choose.'

Help, advice and grants

If you want to ensure that you are saving as much energy as possible, you can get help and advice from a nationwide network of local energy-efficiency advice centres. These can also put you in touch with pro-fessional heating, insulation and glazing installers. It's worth re-membering that the VAT charged by these installers is only 5%, rather than the normal 17.5%. For details of your local centre call 0345 2772000.

Various grants are on offer from the government, energy suppliers and local authorities. Two million people with oil or liquid petroleum gas heating, for example, are entitled to a grant of between £175 and £250 towards the cost of switching to a more efficient condensing boiler. Although grants vary from region to region, the Energy Savings Trust estimates that 51% of homes in Exeter, for example, are eligible for energy-efficiency grants and in some areas that increases to more than 70%.

For details of grants available contact your local energy-efficiency advice centre or check out the EST website – www.saveenergy.co.uk. Its database can pinpoint specific grants available in your area, depending on your particular circumstances.

Loft insulation

By increasing the depth of loft insulation to at least 8 inches (200mm), you can save £45 on your bills each year

Cavity wall insulation

Installing cavity wall insulation will reduce heat loss through your walls by up to 60% and can save you £75-£150 from your annual fuel bills

Double glazing

If you are replacing your windows, go for Double Low E glazing. It costs an extra £275 if fitted by an installer and will save you £30-40 each year

Energy saving lightbulbs

Energy saving lightbulbs only cost about £5 each but save you up to £10 each year

Choice of appliance

Buying an energy-efficient recommended appliance – like a new fridge freezer – could save you up to £450 in running costs over its 10-year lifespan

Heating controls

Adding full heating controls to your central heating system could save up to £85 a year

Maintaining your boiler

Replace unreliable or old boilers and save 30% of your fuel bills. Installing an efficient condensing boiler will save you up to £120 a year

• First appeared in *The Guardian*, October 2000.

© *Helen Jones*

Energy labels

**Energy labels for refrigeration and washing appliances.
Helping you make the right choice.**

By law, the European Community Energy Label must be displayed on all new domestic refrigerators, freezers and fridge-freezer combinations, washing machines, electric tumble dryers, combined washer-dryers and dishwashers displayed for sale, hire or hire-purchase. You should expect to be provided with this information however you buy these products. Mail order catalogues and manufacturers' literature must contain similar information. The scheme is being extended to other appliances.

How to use the energy label to choose more efficient products and save you money

What you get for your money – energy efficiency

The more efficient the product, the less energy it needs to do the same job and the more you get for your money. 'A' rated products are the most efficient and 'G' rated products are the least efficient. Use the main 'A-G' scale to find the best buy. For example, if you were buying a large fridge-freezer, choosing a 'B' rated model to replace a similar 'E' rated model could mean:

- in 1 year – you save £15 in electricity
- in 10 years – you save £150

So, by choosing the more efficient model you can save money on your electricity bills!

How much will it cost to run – energy consumption

This tells you how much electricity this model uses in standard tests. This is given as kWh/year [1] or kWh/cycle [1] depending on the product. You can use this information to work out how much you might save if you choose different machines.

Actual savings will, of course, depend on how you use the appliance and how much you pay for your electricity (the example above assumes you pay 7p/kWh [1] – look at your electricity bill). You can save more money by loading washing machines fully, using economy and low temperature settings, and spin-drying clothes well before you tumble dry; and by ensuring that fridges and freezers are installed away from cookers and other sources of heat – see manufacturer's advice.

Manufacturer's name and product details

This confirms the manufacturer's name and model number – check that this is the same as the model you actually choose to buy.

The European ecolabel

Some products have been awarded the European ecolabel which may appear on the label or elsewhere. The ecolabel indicates that the product has been independently assessed and found to meet strict environmental criteria, putting it among the best in its class. More information about the Eco-labelling Scheme is available at www.environment.detr.gov.uk/ecolabel/index.htm

How well does it perform?

The 'A-G' indicators here are similar to the main energy efficiency ratings and are based on European standards (the test cycle used is on the label) : 'A' is the best performance and 'G' is the worst performance. A washing machine that has a good spin drying performance will save you money and time on tumble drying.

Water consumption, conservation and efficiency

Water consumption

Some appliances use more water than others. All water comes at a cost, both to the environment and to you, the person who pays the bills.

Water conservation

To help you choose an appliance that benefits the environment and your water bills, the figures below show roughly how much water is used by typical household appliances.

Washing machine: 40-135 litres per wash (based on a wash load capacity of 5Kg)

Energy
Manufacturer
Model

ABC
XYZ

More efficient

A
B
C
D
E
F
G

◀ **B**

Less efficient

Energy consumption kWh/year	
(Based on standard test results for 24 h)	**340**
Actual consumption will depend on how the appliance is used and where it is located	
Fresh food volume l	0
Frozen food volume l	170
	✳ ✳✳✳
Noise (dB(A) re 1 pW)	

Further information is contained in product brochures

Norm EN 153 May 1990
Refrigerator Label Directive 94/2/EC

Washer-dryer: 60-240 litres per wash (based on a wash load capacity of 5Kg)

Dishwasher: 12-36 litres per wash (based on an 8-place setting)

Dishwasher: 12-54 litres per wash (based on a 12-place setting)

Water efficiency

Choose an appliance that uses water more efficiently. For example, a washing machine that is designed to use 40 litres per wash rather than 90 litres could reduce your household water bill by 10%, saving you £20 per year on an average metered water bill.

Noise

Manufacturers don't have to provide information on noise but if they do so, this will help you choose a quieter model. The lower the number shown, the quieter the appliance.

No labels?

Ask your retailer first – he must, by law, provide this information. Local authorities are responsible in the UK for enforcing the regulations that cover energy labels and similar energy information in mail order catalogues

etc. You can contact your local Trading Standards Department. Look for 'Trading Standards' under Local Council in the phone book.

For free information on how to 'do your bit' for the environment call our hotline 08457 868686, look on the Doing Your Bit web site www.doingyourbit.org.uk or send your name and address on a postcard to: Are You Doing Your Bit?, P.O. Box 200, Stratford-on-Avon CV37 9BR

For more ways to save money on your energy bills call the Energy Efficient hotline now on 08457 277200 or look on the EST web site www.est.org.uk. 'Energy Efficiency'

is an Energy Saving Trust initiative endorsed by the Government.

Most water companies offer free advice to help you save money on your water bills. For more information, call the Going for Green hotline on 0800 783 7838 or look on the GfG web site at www.gfg.iclnet.co.uk. Going for Green is supported by the Government.

Energy labelling is supported via DETR's Market Transformation Programme. Find out more at www.mtprog.com

Note

1. 'kWh' is a unit of electricity. When you buy electricity, your supplier charges you for how many kWh or 'units' you use. A one-bar electric fire uses 1 kWh in one hour's use. A 100W electric lightbulb uses 1 kWh in 10 hours' use (an energy-saving lightbulb would go on for 40 hours on 1 kWh of electricity!).

• The above is an extract from the Department for the Environment, Transport and the Regions (DETR) web site which can be found at www.detr.gov.uk

Homes with power plants

Homes with power plants could take heat out of global warming

Householders could have fuel-saving, mini power stations fitted in their homes within five years as part of a strategy for tackling global warming unveiled by John Prescott, the Deputy Prime Minister, yesterday.

Mr Prescott announced that Britain will cut its emission of greenhouse gases by 21.5 per cent by 2010 – nearly double the 12.5 per cent legally binding target set by the Kyoto climate change treaty. The programme of changes, which imposes targets on electricity supply companies, but not on the transport industry, will deliver a cut of 17.5 per cent in carbon dioxide, he said.

Mr Prescott said he hoped that the programme would deliver

By Charles Clover, Environment Editor

Labour's manifesto commitment of a 20 per cent cut. Britain is the first country in the world to announce a programme of how it will implement

There is now an obligation on suppliers to deliver 10 per cent of the UK's electricity from renewable sources such as wind, wave and solar power by 2010

the Kyoto target and the first to go far beyond it. Mr Prescott said the disastrous flooding in Mozambique and other extreme weather events round the world underlined the need for firm action to halt climate change.

Michael Meacher, the environment minister, said the industrialised countries were likely to have to cut their fossil fuel emissions by 90 per cent by the 2050s to stabilise climate change and give developing countries with growing populations room for growth. One of the most innovative parts of the Government's strategy is the obligation it has placed on electricity supply companies to save up to 3.8 million tons of carbon a year by improving the energy efficiency of their customers' homes and boilers.

How they do this is up to the supply companies, but one senior official predicted yesterday that within five years companies would find it most effective to offer to fit small combined heat and power plants which would save an estimated quarter of a household's two-ton-a-year fossil fuel emissions compared with a conventional boiler, and an eighth compared with a condensing boiler.

Measures in the Utilities Bill will give ministers the power to set the rate which companies have to spend on energy efficiency as part of their licence agreement. The combination of lower prices because of deregulation and lower VAT has meant that domestic consumption has begun to soar.

Lord Whitty, the junior environment minister, announced the first round of Energy Efficiency Standards of Performance, starting in 2002, which will benefit less well-off households by £22 a year and better-off households by £7 a year and cut carbon emissions by 750,000 tons a year by 2005.

There is now an obligation on suppliers to deliver 10 per cent of the UK's electricity from renewable sources such as wind, wave and solar

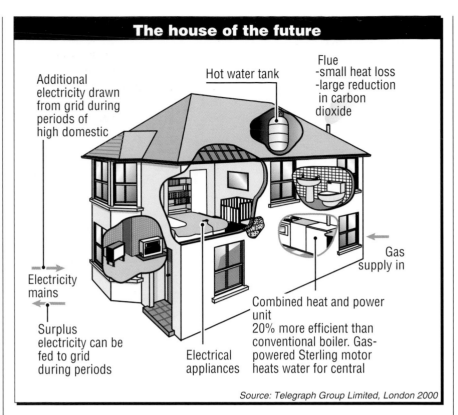

The house of the future

Additional electricity drawn from grid during periods of high domestic

Hot water tank

Flue
-small heat loss
-large reduction in carbon dioxide

Electricity mains

Surplus electricity can be fed to grid during periods

Electrical appliances

Gas supply in

Combined heat and power unit
20% more efficient than conventional boiler. Gas-powered Sterling motor heats water for central

Source: Telegraph Group Limited, London 2000

power by 2010, but the scrapping of the non-fossil fuel levy has cast some doubt on the development of offshore wind farms, one of the most visually-acceptable forms of wind generation.

Eoin Lees, the chief executive of the Energy Saving Trust, said: 'The business sector overall could and should be taking more of the burden of meeting the carbon dioxide targets. It is responsible for almost 50 per cent of greenhouse gas emissions compared with 25 per cent for the domestic sector.'

© Telegraph Group Limited, London 2000

Green electricity

Information from NEF Renewables – The National Energy Foundation

Given the choice
In 1998, the British Government introduced competition into the electricity supply chain, by de-regulating the industry, giving us the choice to buy our electricity from a variety of sources. This will eventually drive down prices as companies compete for customers.

What are green tariffs?
Due to the increase in both awareness and availability of renewable energies there are a range of green tariffs for the domestic consumer. The green tariffs currently available in this country typically involve the payment of an additional premium. There are two types of green tariff available:

1. Renewable Tariff
This is where every unit of electricity bought by a consumer is generated from a renewable energy source.

2. Eco-Funds Tariff
Is where the additional premium is invested in new renewable energy projects. This is in the form of a fund, usually developing community based renewable energy projects.

What is green energy?
Green energy can be loosely defined as energy from renewable or sustainable sources. Examples of green energy include wind power, solar energy, biomass energy and hydro power.

There are also 'waste to energy' projects which can be considered renewable because a large proportion of the energy is derived from biomass (or plant material). There is, however, an argument that queries the sustainability of using waste as a fuel for power generation. Similarly whilst small-scale hydro power is generally considered renewable, the environmental impacts of large scale hydro make it difficult to exploit it sustainably.

Did you know?
Every time we use electricity to switch on a light, or watch television, CO_2 emissions are released into the atmosphere. Purchasing green electricity would avoid this.

Environmentally safer

Conventional forms of electricity produce emissions in the manufacture of electricity, such as sulphur dioxide and carbon dioxide. These pollutants not only add to climate change but can also contribute to acid rain. Electricity produced using renewable energy produces minimal environmental impacts in comparison. Renewable energy is produced from natural resources like water, sun and wind. These renewable energies are an almost limitless supply of power.

The Electrolabel

There are many other countries who are now adopting new schemes which give consumers greater choice. The Electrolabel is one being funded by the European Commission to be the official green accreditation scheme for the EU. The purpose of the scheme is to give consumers the confidence that the electricity they are purchasing comes from environmentally friendly sources.

Clean 'n' Green USA

In USA there are several schemes, with no single scheme as yet being adopted across the board. Studies have revealed that green power accreditation schemes use various criteria. Certification, labelling and tracking are some of the initiatives being looked at. The leading scheme in the USA at present is the Green-e programme which undergoes an annual audit to verify their purchase of renewable energy. It stipulates that at least 50% of their energy comes from renewable sources, and any non-renewable part of the product has lower air emissions than a traditional mix of electricity. Other schemes include the Californian power content label. This is based on the concept of nutrition labels found on food products. Information provided indicates the percentage breakdown of the fuels and technologies used.

Future Energy

Future Energy is an accreditation scheme for the UK, whose aim it is to give consumer confidence in suppliers' claims about their renewable tariffs. The checking process is undertaken by an independent Government-backed organisation. Companies signed up to this scheme are those that supply 100% renewable energy. There are other suppliers, who will offer a mix of renewable energy and conventional electricity.

© NEF Renewables – The National Energy Foundation

So you want to buy green?

Green electricity

The ability to purchase electricity from renewable energy sources is one of the top three incentives to switch power suppliers in the United Kingdom. Fifty-five per cent of households are willing to pay a premium for green power, and 250,000 expect to purchase green power within five years, according to Datamonitor. Consumers are increasingly more educated and selective, and green options now are commonplace within the retail environment, it says. The vast majority are willing to spend up to 2 per cent more for a green tariff.

For many people, the idea of buying their electricity from renewable resources is an attractive one – although it can be slightly more costly than electricity from conventional sources.

Renewable energy has gone through the phases of research and development followed by government support. Now it is entering the market place, and wind power is one of the most feasible of these alternative energy sources. Generating electricity from the wind now makes economic as well as environmental sense.

Since May 1999, electricity consumers have been able to choose whether to go green or stick with dirty 'brown'. The power to choose has led to the development of the green energy market in the domestic as well as global arena. The clear conclusion of this emerging green market is that where there is a choice and the price is right, many prefer the green option.

All green tariffs currently

available involve payment of an additional premium, typically £3-£10 every three months on top of the normal electricity bill. Generally speaking, two types of green tariff are available: 'renewable tariffs', where for every unit of electricity used by a customer, the supplier will buy a unit of electricity from a renewable source; and 'eco funds' where the payment goes into a fund to help develop new renewable energy projects.

Almost all of the 12 regional electricity companies in the UK promote a green tariff in addition to conventional 'brown' power. A handful of independent companies have also joined in, among them BWEA members unit[e] and the first in the field, Ecotricity (Nexgen Group). Ecotricity currently only offer green electricity to business consumers but a similar domestic supply is in development.

To find out which companies offer green tariffs and how green they are, the Friends of the Earth website has collated a Guide to Buying Green Energy which includes information on the tariffs available and also rates them in the Green Energy League table.

The UK government has established an accreditation scheme through the Energy Savings Trust. Future Energy checks on the claims made by companies and rates them accordingly. Phone 020 7222 0101 for a list of accredited suppliers of green energy.

The introduction of new government policy will see electricity suppliers obliged to source increasing proportions of their supply from renewable energy sources or face financial penalties. Along with the Climate Change Levy, green electricity could become the cheaper option – just as it is now less expensive to buy non-polluting unleaded petrol. Already electricity from a large wind farm is cheaper to generate than its 'brown' alternative. Now we can all do our bit to help the environment.

• Taken from *Trends In Renewable Energies* Issue 139 July 2000. The above information is an extract from the British Wind Energy Association's web site which can be found at www.britishwindenergy.co.uk

Our approach to energy for the future

Information from Shell

Our plans for new products and changes in our business portfolio are focused on satisfying the demands of our customers and the broader needs of society – now and in the future. As an energy business, our success will depend on selling the sorts of fuels that society demands. These fuels are gradually moving away from those containing a lot of carbon, such as coal, to those containing less carbon, such as gas. We expect this trend to continue as new fuels such as hydrogen and renewable energy, get cheaper and easier to use.

As expressed in one of our scenarios it is possible that gas and renewables could meet almost 50% of the fuel requirements for power generation in Organisation for Economic Co-operation and Development (OECD) countries by 2020.

Fossil fuels currently meet about 85% of the world's energy needs. There is a great challenge for the energy industry to develop alternative options that are both economic and more environmentally acceptable.

We have been experimenting with renewable energy technologies for 20 years. In 1997, we made a commitment to invest US$500 million over five years to significantly increase the renewables side of our business. For this purpose, we created another core business called 'Shell International Renewables'. Setting up this business is part of our strategic commitment to the development of sustainable energy. In 1999 this was extended when Shell Hydrogen was established to pursue and develop business opportunities related to hydrogen and fuel cells on a global basis.

Detailed information on these new business units can be found in the Shell International Renewables and Shell Hydrogen web sites.

Shell International Renewables
One of the key drivers for developing renewable sources of energy is the desire to reduce carbon dioxide emissions in energy production by gradually replacing fossil fuels such as coal, oil and gas. Renewable sources emit much less carbon dioxide than conventional fuels per unit of energy produced. Many believe they could become a low-cost source of sustainable energy longer term. Shell Renewables is in the third year of a US$ 500 million five-year investment plan to make a profitable business from renewable resources. Success depends on finding enough commercially viable projects. This can be difficult because of the comparatively high cost of harnessing renewable energy sources. A labelling system to certify energy generated in this way could go some way to improve the viability of certain

renewable energy projects. Shell Renewables has so far concentrated on forestry, making and marketing photovoltaic (PV) panels that produce electricity from the sun, and using wood for energy (biomass). In 1999 Renewables began investing in wind energy. This is an update of progress.

Forestry

Shell's hardwood plantation forests cover 140,000 hectares (one hectare is about the area of two football pitches), mainly in South America. The wood is used for paper pulp and, increasingly, for solid wood products.

Shell companies have invested in plantation forestry since the early 1980s and have gained considerable experience in all aspects of the business, including the environmental and social issues. For example, we worked with the World Wide Fund for Nature (WWF) to produce the Tree Plantation Review, a series of twelve reports on a range of social, economic and environmental issues that affect the development of forestry plantations. Shell International Renewables recently prepared revised guidelines for safe working practices and environmental management of tree plantations.

For commercial reasons the business has stopped research into the use of genetic modification in tree improvement. All plantations will seek certification to the independent international standard of the Forest Stewardship Council. Carbon sequestration – the storing of carbon in trees – is under discussion in world forums and the commercial implications are being evaluated.

Biomass energy

Wood is a key source of renewable energy. It is converted into energy by combustion and is ideal for small-scale power stations in the developing world.

Commercial biomass energy contributes more to world primary energy production than all other renewable sources, except for large-scale hydro-electricity. Shell's focus is to produce electricity, heat and solid fuels from sustainable sources of wood, such as plantation forests,

...THEY ARE FROM A MULTINATIONAL ENERGY CORPORATION!

and waste. In Norway, a plant that delivers heat to industry has been upgraded to make wood briquettes for sale. In Denmark wood pellets are sold to consumers. In Europe we want to use the higher efficiencies of combined heat and power plants that burn wood. In Uruguay, we have been researching the most effective way to grow wood fuel.

Wind energy

Wind energy is the fastest growing of all energy sources, at some 25% a year and Shell are keen to establish offshore wind farms. The first pilot project will be at our Harburg refinery in Germany and the electricity generated will be labelled. In the UK two of the largest offshore turbines in the world (2 megawatts each) will be installed shortly.

Solar energy

We expect that the cost of producing photovoltaic panels could drop at the rate of 6-8% per year over the next twenty years. This would mean that, ten years from now, the cost of solar electricity could be a third of what it is today.

The experience of Shell companies with pilot systems in both sunny and cold climates shows how effective and useful the technology can be. However, fossil fuels are currently cheaper to use, so we are working hard to reduce the cost of making solar panels, and looking at new technologies to increase the efficiency of conversion from sunlight to electricity.

Photovoltaic power has many desirable features and is growing rapidly. At present, it represents only a tiny proportion of the world's energy scene, around 0.01% of total supply. Encouraged by some governments in Europe and in Japan, consumers, businesses and local authorities in these markets are erecting solar panels that feed surplus current into the grid. The market is also growing for rural electrification systems and Shell has projects in South Africa, Bolivia, India, Sri Lanka and the Philippines.

Shell produces PV panels in the Netherlands and has recently opened a large factory in Germany. When fully on stream it will be able to make enough PV cells a year to satisfy almost 15% of the current total world market. Some commentators are frustrated at the slow growth in solar power and feel industry should be doing more to bring down costs and stimulate the market, which depends heavily on government subsidy. Without such subsidy solar power would be restricted to specialist applications and some rural electrification schemes. This is a classic 'chicken and egg' situation. Without demand companies are reluctant to invest in large capacity that offers economies of scale. Customers are unwilling to buy until the price comes down. The impasse can be broken by a combination of technical innovation, government incentives, customer willingness to pay more and further investment in production

Shell Hydrogen

Growing environmental awareness and concerns about the sustainability of a hydrocarbon fuel economy have led to a worldwide revival of interest in fuel cells technology.

Shell Hydrogen was established early in 1999 to pursue and develop business opportunities related to hydrogen and fuel cells on a global basis. Shell Hydrogen will provide energy solutions by bringing fuel cells to market promoting a hydrogen reliant fuel economy.

Based in the Netherlands, Shell Hydrogen is the Royal Dutch/Shell Group's sixth global division. The regional bases are in Amsterdam, Houston, Hamburg and Tokyo.

• The above information is from the Shell in the UK web site which can be found at www.shell.com/renewables
© Royal Dutch/Shell Group

Powering up

Turn up the heating today and where does the power come from?

Almost certainly from coal, oil or gas. So-called fossil fuels are warming us and cooking the planet too, but will there ever be earth-friendly energy? Ann Mac-Garry of the Centre for Alternative Technology is optimistic, but not wildly idealistic about the prospects for the future. Here she gives her view on what things might be like in 2020.

Less means more

For a start, we will use less energy. We use energy so wastefully now that we could live quite comfortably using a lot less. This doesn't mean a future of shivering in the semi-dark with no TV. By the year 2020 we could all be living in well-insulated homes, heated by efficient systems. We would be keeping our thermostats at a 'sensible' level so that we'd be wearing a jumper in the winter and we'd be having showers mainly, rather than baths.

We'd be using our washing machines on lower temperatures and not heating the water or cooking with electricity. We wouldn't be using unnecessary electrical devices, such as domestic dishwashers, so we'd be saving the energy used to build those gadgets. The devices we buy will be built to last so that they rarely need replacing. We'll be thinking twice before we buy any objects which will end up as useless rubbish soon after. We will certainly be using private cars less. We will be walking, cycling, using buses and trains and sharing cars or using taxis for those awkward journeys. This will cost people less, so they can spend more on insulating their homes, which will save them money, which they can spend on . . .

Sources of power

The hysterical reaction to wind power will be a thing of the past, as people will have seen from experience that wind farms are a very efficient and cheap way of generating electricity.

They also leave no long-term impact on the land. The UK's first wind farm, put up in 1991, will have reached the end of its expected 25-year lifetime in 2016 and people will have decided either to replace the machines with newer designs or to remove them, leaving nothing but a set of concrete pads and some disappointed sheep which will have nothing to shelter behind in wild weather.

Long before, a national strategy will have been developed to plan what sources of energy we will use and where we'll put them. We will be working towards getting 20% of our electricity from wind power on land, out at sea and probably via wave power. It could be still more in the years to follow. The government will have found the money to build things like tidal power schemes which cost a great deal to build, but produce cheap electricity in the long run. They will have built some small tidal schemes and one across the Mersey estuary, which will be producing half the electricity consumed by Liverpool. People will have realised long before, that although some bird habitats would be changed and reduced in the tidal schemes, those habitats would have disappeared under rising sea levels if we didn't do something to control climate change.

We'll probably have decided to build a couple more large hydro electric schemes like those which have been producing cheap electricity for more than 50 years. We'll certainly have built a lot of small hydro systems as well as some power stations that burn wood.

We'll still be using an old nuclear power station and certainly some fossil fuel ones, but the cost of this electricity will be much higher because there will be taxes added to pay for all the environmental damage caused by using them. So we won't build any nuclear stations and very few fossil fuel ones.

All new houses will use solar energy and will have solar roofs which heat water and generate electricity.

This is a possible future. It is very unlikely that this is what we will be doing, but we could be. It's all technically possible. Making it happen is up to us.

• The above is an extract from the RSPB's web site which can be found at www.rspb.org.uk
© RSPB

ADDITIONAL RESOURCES

You might like to contact the following organisations for further information. Due to the increasing cost of postage, many organisations cannot respond to enquiries unless they receive a stamped, addressed envelope.

British BioGen
Rear North Suite 7th Floor
63-66 Hatton Garden
London, EC1N 8LE
Tel: 020 78317222
Fax: 020 78317223
E-mail: info@britishbiogen.co.uk
Web site: www.britishbiogen.co.uk
Promotes and co-ordinates the commercial development of biomass as a renewable fuel resource for energy production.

British Energy
Barnett Way, Barnwood
Gloucester, GL4 7RS
Tel: 01452 652222
Fax: 01452 652776
Web site: www.british-energy.com
One of the UK's largest electricity companies, it has around 20% of the generation market, and a developing generation business in the US.

British Nuclear Fuels Plc
Information Services
PO Box 100
Warrington, WA4 6FB
Tel: 01925 832000
Web site: www.bnfl.com
BNFL provides high quality, cost-effective nuclear fuel cycle services to customers both at home and overseas.

British Wind Energy Association (BWEA)
26 Spring Street
London, W2 1JA
Tel: 020 7402 7102
Fax: 020 7402 7107
E-mail: info@bwea.com
Web site:
www.britishwindenergy.co.uk
From its early beginnings more than twenty years ago as the professional association for researchers and enthusiasts in the then embryonic wind industry, the British Wind Energy Association has developed into the largest renewable energy trade association in the UK.

Centre for Alternative Technology (CAT)
Machynlleth
Powys, SY20 9AZ
Tel: 01654 702400
Fax: 01654 702782
E-mail: ebost:info@cat.org.uk
Web site: www.cat.org.uk
CAT is a display and education centre. Its seven-acre site has working displays of wind, water and solar power, low energy building, organic growing and alternative sewage systems.

Friends of the Earth (FOE)
26-28 Underwood Street
London, N1 7JQ
Tel: 020 7490 1555
Fax: 020 7490 0881
E-mail: info@foe.co.uk
Web site: www.foe.co.uk
As an independent environmental group, Friends of the Earth publishes a comprehensive range of leaflets, books and in-depth briefings and reports.

Greenpeace
Canonbury Villas
London, N1 2PN
Tel: 020 7865 8100
Fax: 020 7865 8200
E-mail: gn-info@uk.greenpeace.org
Web site: www.greenpeace.org.uk
Greenpeace has 2.9 million supporters in 158 countries; 29 national and three multinational offices worldwide.

National Wind Power
Riverside House
Meadowbank
Furlong Road
Bourne End
Bucks, SL8 5AJ
Tel: 01628 532300
Fax: 01628 531993
E-mail:
webinfo@natwindpower.co.uk
Web site: www.natwindpower.co.uk
National Wind Power is the leading wind farm developer and operator in the UK.

NATTA – Network for Alternative Technology and Technology Assessment
c/o Energy and Environment Research Unit
Open University, Walton Hall
Milton Keynes, MK7 6AA
Tel: 01908 654638
Fax: 01908 858407
Web site: technology.open.ac.uk/eeru/natta/natta-guide.html
NATTA is an independent information service set up in 1976, which focuses on sustainable energy developments and associated issues.

NEF Renewables
The National Energy Foundation
Davy Avenue, Knowlhill
Milton Keynes, MK5 8NG
Tel: 01908 665555
Fax: 01908 665577
E-mail:
renewables@natenerg.demon.co.uk
Web site: www.greenenergy.org.uk
Encourages the efficient use of energy through education and practical projects. Produces educational packs for schools: freephone 0800 1380889.

Shell UK Plc
The Strand
London, WC2R 0DX
Tel: 020 7257 3000
Fax: 020 7257 3835
Web site: www.shell.com/renewables
Shell businesses in the UK are part of the Royal Dutch/Shell Group of companies, one of the largest industrial undertakings in the world.

WWF-UK
Panda House, Weyside Park
Catteshall Lane
Godalming, GU7 1XR
Tel: 01483 426444
Fax: 01483 426409
E-mail: wwf-uk@wwf-uk.org
Web site: www.wwf-uk.org
WWF-UK is the British arm of the largest international conservation organisation in the world.

INDEX

★★★★★

The Internet has been likened to shopping in a supermarket without aisles. The press of a button on a Web browser can bring up thousands of sites but working your way through them to find what you want can involve long and frustrating on-line searches.

And unfortunately many sites contain inaccurate, misleading or heavily biased information. Our researchers have therefore undertaken an extensive analysis to bring you a selection of quality Web site addresses.

British Nuclear Fuels Plc
www.bnfl.com
A very comprehensive web site which covers many aspects of nuclear power. From the home page you can choose options such as News, Facts & Issues, Impact on Society, Research & Technology or the Learning Zone.

Shell UK Plc
www.shell.com/renewables
This is Shell's dedicated Renewables web site. You can choose from links such as Solar, Wind, Biomass and Forestry. You can also view lists of their publications and press releases.

NEF Renewables
www.greenenergy.org.uk
NEF Renewables is the renewable energy department within the National Energy Foundation. From the home page you can choose from Renewable Energy, Green Electricity or News.

DTI New & Renewable Energy Programme
www.dti.gov.uk/renewable/index.html
From the Site Map page you can choose from a number of links within the Introduction to Technologies section. Clicking on Information for Teachers and Students takes you to the **Planet Energy** web site where you can enter The Renewable Energy Trail. Within this there is a choice of sections for students aged 7-11-years-old and 12-16-years-old.

Centre for Alternative Technology (CAT)
www.cat.org.uk
CAT is Europe's foremost Eco-Centre. On their web site you can click on the link Information which includes resources from the centre and sample publications. Click on the Visit us link and you can visit them either in person or virtually using the on-line tour. There is also a tour of other renewable energy sites in Wales.

ACKNOWLEDGEMENTS

The publisher is grateful for permission to reproduce the following material.

While every care has been taken to trace and acknowledge copyright, the publisher tenders its apology for any accidental infringement or where copyright has proved untraceable. The publisher would be pleased to come to a suitable arrangement in any such case with the rightful owner.

Chapter One: Energy Alternatives

Energy – a beginner's guide, © NATTA, *The dinosaur's revenge*, © NATTA, *World fuel shares*, © OECD/IEA, 2000, *Energy consumption*, © 2000 Environment Agency, *Energy consumption*, © Crown copyright is reproduced with the permission of the Controller of Her Majesty's Stationery Office, *Costly energy*, © Friends of the Earth, *Why nuclear energy has to be part of the solution*, © British Energy, *Electricity supplied by fuel type*, © Crown copyright is reproduced with the permission of the Controller of Her Majesty's Stationery Office, *Energy for life*, © British Nuclear Fuels plc, *Producers of nuclear electricity*, © OECD/IEA, 2000, *Nuclear power*, © OneWorld, *New power for Britain*, © Greenpeace, *Renewable energy policy for the UK*, © WWF-UK, *Renewable energy*, © NEF Renewables – The National Energy Foundation, *Go with the flow*, © Guardian Newspapers Limited 2000, *Renewable energy sources*, © Crown copyright is reproduced with the permission of the Controller of Her Majesty's Stationery Office, *National wind power*, © National Wind Power, *Electricity – the facts*, © National Wind Power, *British wind energy*, © British Wind Energy, *The windfarm debate*, © NATTA, *Electricity generating costs*, © The British Wind Energy Association, *Bioenergy – 21st century fuel*, © British BioGen, *A shining example*, © The Centre for Alternative Technology (CAT), *Solar electric power*, © Greenpeace, *BP bows to solar power pressure*, © Guardian Newspapers Limited 2000, *Energy – the changing climate*, © Royal Commission on Environmental Pollution, *Energy targets would change face of Britain*, © Guardian Newspapers Limited 2000, *Wind farms*, © Crown copyright is reproduced with the permission of the Controller of Her Majesty's Stationery Office.

Chapter Two: Energy Efficiency

Positive futures, © Guardian Newspapers Limited 2000, *25 ways to save the planet!*, © Centre for Alternative Technology (CAT), *Act now*, © WWF International, *Money for nothing*, © Helen Jones, *Energy labels*, © Crown copyright is reproduced with the permission of the Controller of Her Majesty's Stationery Office, *Homes with power plants*, © Telegraph Group Limited, London 2000, *Green electricity*, © NEF Renewables – The National Energy Foundation, *So you want to buy green?*, © The British Wind Energy Association, *Our approach to energy for the future*, © Royal Dutch/Shell Group, *Powering up*, © RSPB.

Photographs and illustrations:

Pages 1, 5, 10, 21, 24, 31, 33, 39: Simon Kneebone, pages 12, 19, 23, 25, 32, 37: Pumpkin House.

Craig Donnellan
Cambridge
January, 2001